Second Edition

Test Booklet
Teacher's Edition

James F. Funston
Devon W. Hanahan

Consultant
Alejandro Vargas Bonilla

EMC/Paradigm Publishing, Saint Paul, Minnesota

ISBN 0-8219-1896-6

Published by EMC/Paradigm Publishing
875 Montreal Way
St. Paul, Minnesota 55102
800-328-1452
www.emcp.com
E-mail: educate@emcp.com

Printed in the United States of America
3 4 5 6 7 8 9 10 X X X 05 04 03 02 01 00

Introduction

The *Somos así EN SUS MARCAS* Testing/Assessment Program consist of the following components:

- Test Booklet
- Test Booklet Teacher's Edition
- Four listening comprehension audiocassettes/audio CDs
- Oral Proficiency Evaluation Manual
- Portfolio Assessment

The Test Booklet contains the following: a 100-point test for *Lecciones 1-20*; a 200-point achievement test that covers the content of the textbook through *Capítulo 5*; and a 200-point achievement test for use after students have completed *Capítulos 6-10*. Tests include both a listening comprehension and a written section and are formatted so they may be administered in one day or divided over two days. Suggested point values for test items appear in parentheses at the end of the instructions for each activity.

The listening comprehension section for each test has been recorded on the corresponding *Somos así EN SUS MARCAS* test audiocassette/audio CD. The printed transcript for this portion of each test and the answers for all test items are provided in this Test Booklet Teacher's Edition.

Audiocassette/CD Program Manager
Listening Comprehension Tests

Content	Audiocassette Number	Audiocassette Side	Audio CD Number	Audio CD Track	Time
Capítulo 1					
Lección 1	**1**	**A**	**1**		**13:01**
Test Activity 1	1	A	1	1	1:49
Test Activity 2	1	A	1	2	3:17
Test Activity 3	1	A	1	3	1:13
Test Activity 4	1	A	1	4	1:43
Test Activity 5	1	A	1	5	3:45
Test Activity 6	1	A	1	6	1:14
Lección 2	**1**	**A**	**1**		**9:13**
Test Activity 1	1	A	1	7	1:11
Test Activity 2	1	A	1	8	1:29
Test Activity 3	1	A	1	9	1:27
Test Activity 4	1	A	1	10	1:52
Test Activity 5	1	A	1	11	1:54
Test Activity 6	1	A	1	12	1:20
Capítulo 2					
Lección 3	**1**	**A**	**1**		**7:36**
Test Activity 1	1	A	1	13	1:18
Test Activity 2	1	A	1	14	1:12
Test Activity 3	1	A	1	15	1:03
Test Activity 4	1	A	1	16	2:16
Test Activity 5	1	A	1	17	1:47
Lección 4	**1**	**A**	**1**		**10:43**
Test Activity 1	1	A	1	18	1:14
Test Activity 2	1	A	1	19	2:15
Test Activity 3	1	A	1	20	1:13
Test Activity 4	1	A	1	21	1:29
Test Activity 5	1	A	1	22	3:15
Test Activity 6	1	A	1	23	1:17
Capítulo 3					
Lección 5	**1**	**B**	**1**		**9:03**
Test Activity 1	1	B	1	24	0:56

Content	Audiocassette Number	Audiocassette Side	Audio CD Number	Audio CD Track	Time
Test Activity 2	1	B	1	25	1:13
Test Activity 3	1	B	1	26	1:03
Test Activity 4	1	B	1	27	1:04
Test Activity 5	1	B	1	28	1:02
Test Activity 6	1	B	1	29	1:35
Test Activity 7	1	B	1	30	2:10
Lección 6	**1**	**B**	**1**		**8:20**
Test Activity 1	1	B	1	31	1:23
Test Activity 2	1	B	1	32	1:25
Test Activity 3	1	B	1	33	1:56
Test Activity 4	1	B	1	34	2:05
Test Activity 5	1	B	1	35	1:31
Capítulo 4					
Lección 7	**2**	**A**	**2**		**11:09**
Test Activity 1	2	A	2	1	1:09
Test Activity 2	2	A	2	2	1:51
Test Activity 3	2	A	2	3	1:13
Test Activity 4	2	A	2	4	2:36
Test Activity 5	2	A	2	5	2:37
Test Activity 6	2	A	2	6	1:43
Lección 8	**2**	**A**	**2**		**8:21**
Test Activity 1	2	A	2	7	1:20
Test Activity 2	2	A	2	8	1:48
Test Activity 3	2	A	2	9	1:16
Test Activity 4	2	A	2	10	2:03
Test Activity 5	2	A	2	11	1:54
Capítulo 5					
Lección 9	**2**	**A**	**2**		**6:52**
Test Activity 1	2	A	2	12	1:19
Test Activity 2	2	A	2	13	2:26
Test Activity 3	2	A	2	14	1:18
Test Activity 4	2	A	2	15	1:49

Content	Audiocassette Number	Side	Audio CD Number	Track	Time
Lección 10	**2**	**A**	**2**		**15:23**
Test Activity 1	2	A	2	16	1:48
Test Activity 2	2	A	2	17	3:04
Test Activity 3	2	A	2	18	3:11
Test Activity 4	2	A	2	19	2:01
Test Activity 5	2	A	2	20	3:19
Test Activity 6	2	A	2	21	2:00
Achievement Test I	**2**	**B**	**2**		**19:14**
Test Activity 1	2	B	2	22	1:11
Test Activity 2	2	B	2	23	2:12
Test Activity 3	2	B	2	24	1:06
Test Activity 4	2	B	2	25	0:53
Test Activity 5	2	B	2	26	1:18
Test Activity 6	2	B	2	27	1:12
Test Activity 7	2	B	2	28	1:12
Test Activity 8	2	B	2	29	2:01
Test Activity 9	2	B	2	30	2:42
Test Activity 10	2	B	2	31	1:28
Test Activity 11	2	B	2	32	1:38
Test Activity 12	2	B	2	33	2:21
Capítulo 6					
Lección 11	**3**	**A**	**3**		**11:00**
Test Activity 1	3	A	3	1	1:08
Test Activity 2	3	A	3	2	1:46
Test Activity 3	3	A	3	3	1:58
Test Activity 4	3	A	3	4	3:03
Test Activity 5	3	A	3	5	3:05
Lección 12	**3**	**A**	**3**		**8:18**
Test Activity 1	3	A	3	6	1:45
Test Activity 2	3	A	3	7	1:20
Test Activity 3	3	A	3	8	2:05
Test Activity 4	3	A	3	9	1:55
Test Activity 5	3	A	3	10	1:13

Content	Audiocassette Number	Audiocassette Side	Audio CD Number	Audio CD Track	Time
Capítulo 7					
Lección 13	**3**	**A**	**3**		**9:32**
Test Activity 1	3	A	3	11	1:29
Test Activity 2	3	A	3	12	1:48
Test Activity 3	3	A	3	13	3:15
Test Activity 4	3	A	3	14	1:24
Test Activity 5	3	A	3	15	1:36
Lección 14	**3**	**A**	**3**		**11:48**
Test Activity 1	3	A	3	16	1:52
Test Activity 2	3	A	3	17	1:56
Test Activity 3	3	A	3	18	1:51
Test Activity 4	3	A	3	19	1:09
Test Activity 5	3	A	3	20	2:47
Test Activity 6	3	A	3	21	2:13
Capítulo 8					
Lección 15	**3**	**B**	**3**		**9:11**
Test Activity 1	3	B	3	22	1:17
Test Activity 2	3	B	3	23	1:29
Test Activity 3	3	B	3	24	1:07
Test Activity 4	3	B	3	25	2:18
Test Activity 5	3	B	3	26	3:00
Lección 16	**3**	**B**	**3**		**9:09**
Test Activity 1	3	B	3	27	2:48
Test Activity 2	3	B	3	28	2:10
Test Activity 3	3	B	3	29	1:39
Test Activity 4	3	B	3	30	2:32
Capítulo 9					
Lección 17	**4**	**A**	**4**		**13:18**
Test Activity 1	4	A	4	1	2:33
Test Activity 2	4	A	4	2	2:27
Test Activity 3	4	A	4	3	1:35
Test Activity 4	4	A	4	4	1:39
Test Activity 5	4	A	4	5	5:04

Content	Audiocassette Number	Audiocassette Side	Audio CD Number	Audio CD Track	Time
Lección 18	**4**	**A**	**4**		**11:56**
Test Activity 1	4	A	4	6	1:32
Test Activity 2	4	A	4	7	1:53
Test Activity 3	4	A	4	8	1:35
Test Activity 4	4	A	4	9	2:13
Test Activity 5	4	A	4	10	2:28
Test Activity 6	4	A	4	11	2:15
Capítulo 10					
Lección 19	**4**	**A**	**4**		**11:18**
Test Activity 1	4	A	4	12	1:31
Test Activity 2	4	A	4	13	1:47
Test Activity 3	4	A	4	14	1:59
Test Activity 4	4	A	4	15	2:12
Test Activity 5	4	A	4	16	3:49
Lección 20	**4**	**A**	**4**		**9:23**
Test Activity 1	4	A	4	17	1:33
Test Activity 2	4	A	4	18	1:32
Test Activity 3	4	A	4	19	1:50
Test Activity 4	4	A	4	20	2:08
Test Activity 5	4	A	4	21	2:20
Achievement Test II	**4**	**B**	**4**		**17:05**
Test Activity 1	4	B	4	22	2:26
Test Activity 2	4	B	4	23	1:46
Test Activity 3	4	B	4	24	2:04
Test Activity 4	4	B	4	25	1:17
Test Activity 5	4	B	4	26	2:16
Test Activity 6	4	B	4	27	1:24
Test Activity 7	4	B	4	28	2:11
Test Activity 8	4	B	4	29	3:41

CAPÍTULO 1

Lección 1

Listening Comprehension Test

1. **You will hear several sentences in Spanish. Each will be repeated. The second time you hear the sentence, fill in the blank with the missing word. Be sure to add appropriate punctuation or accents marks where necessary. (6 points)**

   1. ¡Hola! ¿Cómo te llamas?
   2. Me llamo Andrés.
   3. ¡Mucho gusto, Andrés!
   4. ¿Cómo se escribe Andrés?
   5. Se escribe con a mayúscula, ene, de, ere e con acento ese.

2. **You will hear several winning lottery numbers. Circle the number you hear in each group. You will hear each winning number twice. (8 points)**

1.	uno, tres, uno, dos, uno, cuatro	B
2.	dos, nueve, siete, seis, tres, ocho	A
3.	siete, tres, dos, dos, cero, uno	C
4.	cuatro, tres, siete, cero, ocho, siete	B
5.	cero, nueve, uno, cinco, dos, cero	A
6.	ocho, nueve, siete, seis, cinco, tres	A
7.	cuatro, tres, tres, cuatro, cero, uno	B
8.	cinco, cero, nueve, dos, uno, ocho	C

3. **Listen carefully to some things that Señora Suárez says to her students in class. If she is talking to a boy, circle the word *muchacho*. If she is talking to a girl, circle the word *muchacha*. (7 points)**

1.	Hola, Mateo.	muchacho
2.	Adiós, Carmen.	muchacha
3.	¡Mucho gusto, Javier!	muchacho
4.	¿Cómo se escribe Esteban?	muchacho
5.	Hasta luego, Marisol.	muchacha
6.	Adiós, Dolores.	muchacha
7.	Hola, Julio.	muchacho

4. **Listen carefully to the following pairs of sentences. They will not be repeated. If the second sentence is a logical response to the first, circle the letter *L*. If it is illogical, circle the letter *I*. (8 points)**

1.	Adiós, Pedro. Se escribe con ge mayúscula.	I
2.	¡Hola! ¿Y tú?	I
3.	Me llamo José. ¿Cómo te llamas? Me llamo Julia.	L

4. ¿Cómo se escribe Juanita? ¿Con jota?
   Mucho gusto, Juanita. I
5. Adiós Guillermo.
   Hasta luego, Mercedes. L
6. ¿Cuántos años tienes?
   Tengo ocho. L
7. ¿De dónde eres?
   Sí, soy de aquí. I
8. ¿Te llamas Lucía?
   No, me llamo Susana. L

5. Imagine you have a summer job taking reservations for the Hotel San Marcos in Madrid. Listen as eight people spell their last names in Spanish two times. Write each name you hear in the space provided. (8 points)

1. Albarracín 2. Morales 3. Chemás 4. Gutiérrez 5. Hurtado 6. Juárez 7. Yepes 8. Allende

6. You will hear several expressions in Spanish. Write the letter of the illustration that best relates to what you hear. (6 points)

1. ¡Hola! A
2. Hasta luego. B
3. ¿Cómo te llamas? A
4. Adiós. B
5. ¡Mucho gusto! A
6. Me llamo Sergio. A

END OF LISTENING COMPREHENSION TEST

Written Test

7. Find the pattern and then write the missing numbers in Spanish. (5 points)

1. cuatro 2. siete 3. nueve 4. doce 5. cinco

8. Circle the word or expression that does not belong in each of the following groups of three. (8 points)

1. Hola. 2. Jaime 3. Esperanza 4. Lima 5. Portugal 6. de 7. año 8. me llamo

9. Complete the conversation you might have as you meet a new student, choosing from the following words: *adiós, me, te, luego, llamo, llamas, hola, yo, tú.* (8 points)

1. Hola 2. te 3. llamas 4. llamo 5. tú 6. Me 7. luego 8. Adiós

10. Look at the map and match each person's name with the letter of the country he or she is from. (10 points)

1. D 2. K 3. I 4. G 5. B 6. C 7. H 8. E 9. A 10. L

11. **Diego and Carlota are meeting each other on the first day of school. Arrange the following sentences in logical order from A-G to form a dialog between them. One sentence has been placed in the correct order for you as a model. (6 points)**

    1. F 2. C 3. D 4. E 5. (A) 6. B 7. G

12. **Read the following statements carefully, deciding whether each one is true or false. Write the letter *C (cierto)* if the statement is true or *F (falso)* if it is false. (8 points)**

    1. F 2. C 3. C 4. F 5. C 6. C 7. F 8. C

13. **Answer the following questions in Spanish, using complete sentences. (8 points)**

    Possible answers:
    1. Me llamo (*student's name*). 2. Soy de *(place of origin).* 3. Tengo (#) años.
    4. Se escribe con *(spelling of student's name).*

14. **In English, write four benefits to learning Spanish. (4 points)**
    Answers will vary.

CAPÍTULO 1

Lección 2

Listening Comprehension Test

1. **Listen carefully to the following telephone numbers as they are read aloud and circle the one you hear in each group. You will hear each telephone number once only. (5 points)**

1. 42-09-70	B
2. 15-23-50	A
3. 26-01-10	A
4. 83-99-03	C
5. 41-01-86	B

2. **Listen carefully to the following sentences. They will not be repeated. Then circle the letter of the most appropriate response to each expression. (8 points)**

1. ¿Qué tal?	A
2. Buenas tardes.	B
3. ¿Cómo está Ud., señora?	A
4. Buenas noches, señor Camacho.	C
5. ¿Cómo están Uds.?	A
6. ¿Cómo estás tú?	A
7. Adiós.	C
8. Hasta luego.	B

3. **Decide whether the following clocks tell time accurately or not. If the time you hear matches the time you see on the clock, circle *sí*. If they do not match, circle *no*. (8 points)**

1. Son las cinco.	sí
2. Son las once menos cuarto.	no
3. Son las diez y media.	sí
4. Son las siete menos veinte.	sí
5. Son las ocho y cinco.	sí
6. Es la una y veinte.	no
7. Son las tres menos cinco.	no
8. Es la una menos cuarto.	sí

4. **Listen carefully to the following pairs of sentences. They will not be repeated. If the second sentence is a logical response to the first, circle the letter *L*. If it is illogical, circle the letter *I*. (9 points)**

1. Buenas noches. Regular.	I
2. ¡Hola, Ana! ¿Qué tal? Bien, gracias.	L
3. Buenos días, Sra. Medina. Muy bien, gracias.	I
4. Estoy regular. ¿Y tú? ¡Hola!	I
5. ¿Qué tal, Paco? Hasta pronto.	I
6. Buenos días, Srta. Echeverría. Buenos días, Sr. Iglesias.	L
7. Hasta mañana. Adiós.	L
8. ¿Cómo están Uds.? Muy bien, gracias.	L
9. Hola, Dolores. ¡Hola! ¿Qué tal?	L

5. **You will hear several sentences in Spanish. Write the letter of the illustration that best relates to what you hear. (10 points)**

1. ¡Hola, Margarita! ¿Qué tal?	C
2. ¡Buenos días, Enrique!	A
3. Estoy mal, muy mal.	A
4. Es mediodía.	B
5. ¡Buenas noches, Marta!	C
6. Perdón, ¿qué hora es?	C
7. Buenas tardes, Ramón.	B
8. Son las seis de la mañana.	A
9. Es medianoche.	C
10. Con permiso, Sra. Ruiz.	B

6. **You will hear several sentences in Spanish. Each will be repeated. The second time you hear the sentence, fill in each blank with the missing word. You may choose to use abbreviations when appropriate. (6 points)**

   1. Buenos días, señora/Sra. Rodríguez.
   2. ¿Cómo está usted/Ud.?
   3. Muy bien, gracias, señorita/Srta.Tovar.
   4. Hasta luego.

END OF LISTENING COMPREHENSION TEST

Written Test

7. **Complete each of the following sentences logically using *tú, usted or ustedes.* (8 points)**

   1. tú 2. usted 3. ustedes 4. tú 5. usted 6. ustedes 7. usted 8. tú

8. **Greet the following people in Spanish. Then ask them how they are. Follow the model. (8 points)**

   1. Buenos días, Sr. Bernal. ¿Cómo está Ud.? 2. Buenos días, Mateo y Blanca. ¿Cómo están Uds.? 3. Buenas tardes, Srta. Sánchez. ¿Cómo está Ud.? 4. Buenas noches, Carlota. ¿Cómo estás?/¿Qué tal?

9. **In the space provided, write the letter of the nickname that corresponds to each name. (6 points)**

   1. E 2. B 3. D 4. F 5. C 6. A

10. **In the space provided, write the time you see on each clock in Spanish. (6 points)**

    1. Son las diez. 2. Son las seis menos cuarto. 3. Son las dos y media. 4. Son las tres y cinco. 5. Son las nueve menos cinco. 6. Es la una y veinte.

11. **Arrange the following sentences in logical order from A-G to form a dialog between Pilar and Señora Torres. Two sentences have been placed in their correct order for you as models. (5 points)**

    1. (C) 2. (E) 3. F 4. G 5. A 6. B 7. D

12. **Complete the conversation between Inés and Señor Acuña choosing from the following words: *gracias, días, tarde, noche, perdón, tú, usted, es, son, nada, está, estás, muy, qué.* (10 points)**

    1. días 2. estás 3. gracias 4. usted 5. Muy 6. Perdón 7. qué 8. Es 9. tarde 10. nada

13. **Choose the expression in Spanish that you would say in each given situation and write it in the blank provided. (5 points)**

    1. De nada./Con mucho gusto. 2. Dos, por favor. 3. Perdón. Lo siento. 4. Con permiso. 5. Muchas gracias.

14. **Answer the following questions in Spanish, using complete sentences. (6 points)**

Possible answers:
1. Estoy bien. 2. Sí, (No, no) estoy muy bien. 3. Es la/ Son las (*time*).

CAPÍTULO 2

Lección 3

Listening Comprehension Test

1. **You will hear several short statements about items in a classroom. Write the letter that corresponds with each object you hear. (6 points)**

1. Es una regla.	F
2. Son unos lápices.	B
3. Es un pupitre.	D
4. Son unas sillas.	A
5. Son unos bolígrafos.	C
6. Es una mochila.	E

2. **You will hear several sentences about people and objects. If the person or object mentioned is masculine, circle *M*. If the person or object mentioned is feminine, circle *F*. (7 points)**

1. Es una pared.	F
2. ¿Quién es la chica?	F
3. ¿De dónde es el profesor?	M
4. ¿Cómo se llama el estudiante?	M
5. Es el mapa de Ecuador.	M
6. La silla es nueva.	F
7. Es un pupitre.	M

3. **You will hear some questions. They will not be repeated. Circle the letter of the logical response for each. (5 points)**

1. ¿De dónde es Pedro?	B
2. ¿De dónde eres tú?	A
3. ¿De dónde es Claudia?	A
4. ¿Es él de Chile?	B
5. ¿Eres tú de España?	B

4. **Listen carefully to the following pairs of sentences. They will not be repeated. If the second sentence is a logical response to the first, circle the letter *L*. If it is illogical, circle the letter *I*. (10 points)**

1. Me llamo Esteban ¡Mucho gusto!	L
2. ¿De dónde eres? ¿Eres tú de aquí?	I

3. ¿Eres de Venezuela? L
   Sí, soy de Caracas.
4. ¿Quién es ella? I
   Ella es de San Juan.
5. ¿Es ella una estudiante nueva? L
   Sí, ella es una estudiante nueva.
6. ¿Es el estudiante nuevo de Miami? I
   Sí, hay nueve.
7. ¿Quién es él? L
   Él se llama Roberto Morales.
8. ¿De dónde son Pilar y Alberto? L
   Son de Puerto Rico.
9. ¿Quién es la estudiante con la mochila? I
   La mochila es de mi amiga.
10. ¿Qué quiere decir "libro"? L
    Quiere decir "book".

5. **You will hear six questions. The answers to all six questions follow but are not in their correct order. When each question is repeated, write the letter of the most appropriate answer in the space provided. (6 points)**

1. ¿Cómo se llama Ud.? E
2. ¿Es él de Colombia? A
3. ¿Eres de México? C
4. ¿Te llamas Raúl? D
5. ¿Cómo se llama él? B
6. ¿Es ella de aquí? F

END OF LISTENING COMPREHENSION TEST

Written Test

6. **In the space provided, write the correct definite article (*el, la, los* or *las*) for each of the following nouns. (10 points)**

   1. el 2. el 3. las 4. el 5. el 6. la 7. la 8. los 9. las 10. los

7. **Identify the items shown in this illustration. Include the appropriate indefinite articles *un* or *una* in your answers. Follow the model. (10 points)**

   1. un cesto de papeles 2. un reloj 3. una puerta 4. una pizarra 5. un cuaderno

8. **Jorge says the opposite of everything he hears. Show what he says by rewriting the following sentences so they are negative. Follow the model. (4 points)**

   1. No soy de México. 2. El estudiante nuevo no se llama Ramón. 3. Ellos no son de Miami, Florida. 4. No sé mi número de teléfono.

9. **Arrange the following sentences in logical order from *A-E* to form a dialog between Marta and Arturo. The first one has been done for you. (4 points)**

   1. (E) 2. C 3. D 4. A 5. B

10. **Imagine you are talking with a new member of a city-wide Spanish club where you are a club officer. In the space provided, write the Spanish subject pronoun that corresponds to the verb form in the sentence to tell new club members where various people are from. (5 points)**

    1. Nosotros,-as 2. Ella 3. Tú 4. Ellos 5. Él

11. **Complete the following dialog, using the words shown. (8 points)**

    1. llama 2. gusto 3. Mucho 4. Es 5. Soy 6. Ud. 7. Yo 8. Unidos

12. **Imagine the following are answers to questions you overheard at a party you attended. Write the questions that might have prompted their answers. (8 points)**

    Possible questions:
    1. ¿De dónde eres tú/es Ud.? 2. ¿Cómo se llama ella? 3. ¿Eres tú/es Ud. de aquí?
    4. ¿Qué quiere decir "libro"?

13. **Read this paragraph about the new girl in school. Then circle the letter of the correct response for each question that follows. (3 points)**

    1. B 2. A 3. A

14. **You have learned many ways in which Hispanic culture has influenced American culture. Show your knowledge by indicating the following information. (6 points)**

    Answers will vary.

15. **Answer the following questions in Spanish, using complete sentences. (8 points)**

    Possible answers:
    1. Sí (No, no), soy de España. 2. Soy de (los) Estados Unidos. 3. Se dice "libro".
    4. Quiere decir *friend.*

CAPÍTULO 2

Lección 4

Listening Comprehension Test

1. Listen to the following sentences about certain classroom items. They will not be repeated. If you hear a color describing the item in the sentence, circle *sí*. If you do not hear a color in the sentence, circle *no*. (5 points)

1. El lápiz es amarillo.	sí
2. El bolígrafo es nuevo.	no
3. El escritorio gris está en la clase.	sí
4. La impresora roja es nueva.	sí
5. La tiza está en la pizarra.	no

2. Imagine that you are a secretary taking telephone messages that consist of the caller's name and various numbers. Listen to each message and fill in the missing part of each number. When you hear the message a second time, circle the appropriate letter to indicate whether it is a phone number, fax number or cell phone number. (8 points)

1. Soy Amalia Pérez y mi número de teléfono celular es el 8-79-<u>99</u>-51.	C
2. Soy Verónica Gómez y mi número de teléfono es el 8-<u>76</u>-01-55.	A
3. Soy Esteban Giraldo y mi número de fax es el 8-84-25-<u>15</u>.	B
4. Soy el Dr. Sánchez y mi número de teléfono es el 8-<u>81</u>-54-07.	A

3. You will hear several statements or questions about schedules. Write the letter of the clock that represents the time you hear in each statement or question. (5 points)

1. ¿Hay una clase a las doce?	E
2. La clase de español es a las diez y once de la mañana.	B
3. ¿Qué clase hay a las diez menos cuarto?	C
4. ¿Qué clase hay a las once y media de la mañana?	A
5. ¿Dónde estás a las cinco menos doce de la tarde?	D

4. Listen to Ana as she describes her study schedule. Then write the day for each class she names. (5 points)

1. Estudio matemáticas los lunes.	lunes
2. Estudio inglés los viernes.	viernes
3. Estudio español los martes.	martes
4. Estudio arte los miércoles.	miércoles
5. ¿La biología? ¡Ay! Estudio biología los sábados.	sábados

5. **Listen carefully to the following short dialogs. They will not be repeated. Each conversation will be followed by one question about the conversation. Circle the letter of the appropriate response. (8 points)**

1. LUIS: ¿Dónde está mi libro?
   DIEGO: No está en mi mochila.
   MARÍA: Mira, Luis, está aquí en el pupitre.

   ¿Dónde está el libro? B

2. IGNACIO: Por favor, ¿qué quiere decir la palabra *keyboard*?
   SRA. MORALES: La palabra *keyboard* quiere decir "teclado".

   ¿Qué quiere decir la palabra "teclado"? A

3. ELISA: Por favor, ¿cómo se dice *screen* y *mouse* en español?
   SR. CHÁVEZ: Se dice "pantalla" y "ratón".

   ¿Cómo se dice *screen* en español? A

4. AMPARO: ¿Dónde está mi papel?
   MARIO: Está en el cesto de papeles.
   AMPARO: No. Mira, está aquí.
   MARIO: ¿Dónde?
   AMPARO: En el escritorio de la profesora.

   ¿Dónde está el papel de Amparo? B

5. SONIA: El borrador está en la pizarra.
   ALBERTO: Los papeles están en el libro de historia.
   DOMINGO: El mapa está en la pared.

   ¿Dónde está el borrador? A

6. MAURICIO: Nosotros estudiamos inglés. ¿Qué estudian Roberto y Luis?
   CONSUELO: Ellos estudian biología.
   MAURICIO: Yo no estudio biología.

   ¿Qué estudian Roberto y Luis? B

7. QUIQUE: ¿A qué hora es la clase de computación?
   AMALIA: Es a las dos.
   QUIQUE: Y ¿a qué hora termina la clase?
   AMALIA: Termina a las tres menos cinco.

   ¿A qué hora es la clase de computación? A

8. PROFESOR ARDILA: ¿Cuántos pupitres hay en la clase?
   ANTONIO: Hay treinta.
   PROFESOR ARDILA: Y ¿cuántos estudiantes hay?
   ANTONIO: Hay cuarenta y dos.

   ¿Cuántos pupitres hay? A

6. **In the space provided, write the letter of the item that best corresponds to each statement or question that you hear. (6 points)**

    1. ¿Dónde está el ratón? D
    2. El horario está en la pantalla. C
    3. ¿Es nueva la computadora? A
    4. Hay un diskette en el escritorio. B
    5. Alberto necesita la impresora. F
    6. El teclado es blanco. E

END OF LISTENING COMPREHENSION TEST

Written Test

7. **Complete the following statements, choosing the adjective that most logically complete each sentence. Remember that adjectives agree in number and gender with the noun it describes. (5 points)**

    1. rojos 2. negra 3. verdes 4. gris 5. nuevos

8. **Complete the following sentences with the appropriate forms of the verb *estar* to indicate where Miguel and several Internet pals are right now. (5 points)**

    1. estoy 2. estamos 3. está 4. están 5. estás

9. **Complete these sentences logically, choosing from the words in the box. Not all answer choices are used. (5 points)**

    1. termina 2. estudia 3. está 4. necesita 5. habla

10. **Complete the following paragraph with the conjugated forms of the verb *hablar* to indicate who talks on the telephone with whom in Jaime's class. Choose from: *habla, hablo, hablamos, hablas, hablan.* (5 points)**

    1. hablo 2. hablamos 3. hablan 4. habla 5. hablas

11. **Timoteo makes several observations about his classroom, but they are incomplete. Complete them by filling in the second sentence in each pair with the same descriptive information from the first. Remember to make the nouns and adjectives agree. (5 points)**

    1. blanco 2. negras 3. verde 4. unas estudiantes nuevas 5. grises

12. **Complete the dialog between Javier and Daniel, choosing from the words or phrases shown below. Some answer choices may not be used. (9 points)**

    1. está 2. Hay 3. Quién 4. se llama 5. De 6. sé 7. clase 8. estudia
    9. señora

13. **Scan the following excerpt from *El león y el grillito*, an Aztec legend about a race between a lion and a cricket. Find three infinitives that end in *-ar* and write them in the space provided. (3 points)**

Possible answers:
llamar, conversar, cantar, trabajar, enseñar, matar

14. **Imagine that you are a student at San Martín High School in Mexico. Your key pal is asking you questions about your school day. Look at your schedule and answer the questions that follow in complete sentences. (10 points)**

1. Tengo seis clases los lunes. 2. El almuerzo es a las doce. 3. Estudio español a la una y media los miércoles. 4. Estudio biología. 5. Hay ocho clases.

15. **Read the following statements carefully, deciding whether each one is true or false. Write the letter C if the statement is true or F if it is false. (8 points)**

1. F 2. C 3. F 4. C 5. F 6. F 7. C 8. C

16. **Answer the following questions in Spanish, using complete sentences. (8 points)**

Possible answers:
1. Mi libro de español está en (*place*). 2. Yo estudio (*subject*). 3. Hay (*number*) estudiantes.
4. Es a las (*time*).

CAPÍTULO 3

Lección 5

Listening Comprehension Test

1. **You will hear several introductions. They will not be repeated. Circle the letter of the logical response for each. (4 points)**

1. Javier y María, les presento a mi amiga, María.	A
2. Esteban, te presento a mi amiga, Lola.	B
3. Don Marcos, le presento a mi madre.	A
4. Paco, te presento a Miguel.	B

2. **Listen carefully to the following introductions. If the person making the introductions uses the correct form of *le, te* or *les* for the person being introduced, circle *correcta.* If the sentence is incorrect, circle *incorrecta.* (5 points.)**

1. Raquel, te presento a Andrés.	correcta
2. Sra. Rodríguez, te presento a mi amiga, Pilar.	incorrecta
3. Sr. Vega, le presento a Juan.	correcta
4. Carmen y Antonio, te presento a la Srta. Botero.	incorrecta
5. Srta. López y Sr. Andrade, les presento a Consuelo.	correcta

3. Can you tell when someone is asking you a question? Listen carefully to the following sentences. Circle *sí* if you hear a question or circle *no* if you don't hear a question. (5 points)

1. ¿Quién es? — sí
2. ¿Van Uds. a la fiesta? — sí
3. No voy porque no tengo transporte. — no
4. ¿Por qué no vas al médico? — sí
5. El número de teléfono es el dos, setenta, cero, siete, sesenta y cuatro. — no

4. You will hear some questions. They will not be repeated. Circle the letter of the logical response for each. (5 points)

1. ¿Adónde vas tú? — A
2. ¿Cómo va Pedro a la oficina? — B
3. ¿Van a pie? — B
4. ¿Por qué vamos en avión? — A
5. ¿Cuándo va ella a España? — B

5. Listen carefully to the following pairs of sentences. They will not be repeated. If the second sentence is a logical response to the first, circle the letter *L*. If it is illogical, circle the letter *I*. (4 points)

1. ¿Vas a la fiesta de Mario? — I
   Sí, vas con Anita.
2. ¿Por qué no vas tú? — L
   Porque no tengo transporte.
3. ¿Va Paco en carro? — I
   Es la cafetería.
4. ¿Es cerca de aquí? — I
   El carro es de Paco.

6. In the space provided, write the letter of the illustration that best corresponds to the place you hear in each of the following questions. (8 points)

1. ¿Quién va al banco? — C
2. ¿Ella va al hotel? — E
3. ¿Quién va al dentista? — H
4. ¿Va Teresa al cine a las nueve? — D
5. Vamos a la escuela en camión hoy, ¿verdad? — F
6. ¿Va la señora González al parque? — A
7. ¿Tú y yo vamos a la biblioteca con ellos? — G
8. ¿Vas tú a la médica? — B

7. Listen as several people tell about some activities and events. The information will then be repeated. After each person finishes, you will hear two questions. Circle the letter of the logical response for each. (6 points)

Hoy es la fiesta de Sara. La fiesta es a las nueve y media. Juan va en el carro de Óscar porque la fiesta es muy lejos.

1. ¿Cuándo es la fiesta de Sara? — A
2. ¿A qué hora es la fiesta? — B

Mi amigo, Paco, es de México. Yo soy de San Diego. Él y yo vamos a México. Vamos en carro porque no está lejos de San Diego.

3. ¿Adónde van los muchachos? A
4. ¿Por qué van en carro? B

Me llamo Jorge Ruíz. Voy al cine. Voy a pie porque está muy cerca. Mis amigos van al cine también. Ellos van en autobús porque está muy lejos.

5. ¿Adónde va Paco a pie? B
6. ¿Cómo van los amigos al cine? A

END OF LISTENING COMPREHENSION TEST

Written Test

8. Complete the following sentences with the following words or groups of words: *al, a la, a los, a las, del, de la, de los, de las.* (8 points)

1. a las 2. a los 3. a la 4. al 5. del 6. del 7. de la 8. de los

9. Determine if the following sentences require a definite article. Then complete the sentences, adding *el, la, los* or *las* in the space provided. If a sentence does not require a definite article, place an *X* in the space. (6 points)

1. X 2. la 3. El 4. X 5. X 6. los

10. Complete the following sentences logically in Spanish, indicating each means of transportation shown in the corresponding illustrations. (6 points)

1. barco 2. moto(cicleta) 3. tren 4. pie 5. avión 6. caballo

11. Indicate where the following people are going by completing these sentences, choosing from the following words: *voy, vas, va, vamos, van.* (5 points)

1. vamos 2. va 3. va 4. voy 5. van

12. Complete the following sentences with the appropriate Spanish question-asking words. (5 points)

Possible answers:
1. Dónde 2. Cómo 3. Cuándo 4. Por qué 5. Adónde

13. Rewrite the following statements in Spanish in question form. (4 points)

1. ¿Es Julia la amiga de Héctor? 2. ¿Van Uds. al banco? 3. ¿Es el señor Durán mi profesor de matemáticas? 4. ¿Va Lourdes al cine?

14. **Using one of the interrogative words listed below, write appropriate questions in Spanish for each of the following statements. (8 points)**

    1. ¿De dónde son ellos? 2. ¿A qué hora van ellos? 3. ¿Cuál es tu número de teléfono? 4. ¿Dónde está Ramón?

15. **Read the following statements carefully, deciding whether each one is true or false. Write the letter *C* if the statement is true or *F* if it is false. (6 points)**

    1. C 2. F 3. F 4. C 5. C 6. C

16. **Use the cues to say where the indicated people are going to go tomorrow and how they are going to arrive there. (6 points)**

    1. Nosotros vamos al cine en metro. 2. Yo voy al parque en bicicleta. 3. Arturo va a la biblioteca en carro.

17. **Read the following biographical information about Lucila de Vargas. Then complete the statements that follow. (5 points)**

    1. Luci y Luz 2. (los) Estados Unidos 3. a pie/ a las ocho y media de la mañana 4. veintiocho muchachos 5. a la fiesta de Lili

18. **Answer the following questions in Spanish, using complete sentences. You may make up any information you wish. (4 points)**

    Possible answers:
    1. Voy a mi colegio en autobús (en metro, a pie, en carro). 2. Mañana voy a(l)...en/a....

CAPÍTULO 3

Lección 6

Listening Comprehension Test

1. **Listen carefully to the following statements about several people. Circle the letter of the subject pronoun that matches the verb form for each sentence you hear. (6 points)**

Modelo: Vamos a un restaurante.	B
1. Hago una pregunta en la clase.	B
2. No comemos el pescado.	A
3. Sabe mi número de teléfono, ¿verdad?	B
4. ¿Leen el periódico ahora?	B
5. Ves un edificio grande.	B
6. Comprende el mapa de la ciudad.	A

2. Listen carefully to the following statements about people's activities. If you hear that the activity is taking place now, circle *ahora.* If you hear that the activity is taking place tomorrow, circle *mañana.* (7 points)

1.	Enrique va a tomar un refresco.	mañana
2.	Tú lees un libro de historia.	ahora
3.	Vamos a hacer un pollo con mole.	mañana
4.	Voy a comer en un restaurante mexicano.	mañana
5.	El mesero habla con la cantante.	ahora
6.	Los estudiantes ven un museo en la plaza.	ahora
7.	Van a ir al concierto de Luis Miguel.	mañana

3. In the space provided, write the letter of the illustration that best corresponds to each description you hear. (10 points)

1.	Es un edificio grande, ¿verdad?	A
2.	El mesero toma agua mineral.	B
3.	Los estudiantes leen un libro ahora.	C
4.	Estamos en la Avenida Mayor.	A
5.	¿Hay una tienda cerca de la plaza?	A
6.	Voy a comer el pollo y los frijoles.	B
7.	Ana hace una pregunta en español.	C
8.	¡Él es mi cantante favorito!	B
9.	Necesito el menú, por favor.	B
10.	Hay muchos edificios grandes.	A

4. Listen carefully to the following pairs of sentences. They will not be repeated. If the second sentence is a logical response to the first, circle the letter L. If it is illogical, circle the letter I. (10 points)

1.	¿Cómo vas a ir al centro? Voy a tomar el autobús.	L
2.	¿Qué vas a hacer en el centro? Voy ahora.	I
3.	¿Dónde está el museo? Está en la Calle Juárez.	L
4.	¿Cuándo vamos al concierto? Es mi cantante favorito.	I
5.	¿Dónde está el restaurante Los Adobes? No sé.	L
6.	¿Por qué no vamos al centro hoy? Sí, ¡vamos!	L
7.	Voy a tomar un jugo de naranja. ¿Y tú? Sí, hay muchas tiendas en el centro.	I
8.	No veo el Teatro Real. Vamos en carro.	I
9.	¿Qué hace Alberto? Lee el periódico.	L
10.	¿Ves el banco? Sí, está aquí en la Avenida Robles.	L

5. **You will hear six questions, each of which will be repeated. Circle the letter of the logical response for each. (6 points)**

1. ¿Dónde está el teatro?	A
2. ¿Vamos a ir al concierto mañana?	B
3. ¿Qué vas a hacer en el centro?	B
4. ¿Va José a comer pescado?	A
5. ¿Por qué no vamos a la tienda grande en la calle Mayor?	B
6. ¿Ves un restaurante en la plaza?	A

END OF LISTENING COMPREHENSION TEST

Written Test

6. **Circle the letter of the word in each group that most logically does not belong. (8 points)**

   1. D 2. B 3. A 4. C 5. A 6. D 7. A 8. B

7. **Complete the dialogue choosing from the words or phrases shown. Some answer choices may not be used. (10 points)**

   1. concierto 2. favorito 3. vamos 4. Cuándo 5. pero 6. voy 7. comer 8. acuerdo 9. Dónde 10. centro

8. **Combine the words and expressions from each of the three columns in a logical manner to tell what four people are going to do in the city and where they are going to do their activities. Add words and make the necessary changes. Follow the model. (12 points)**

   Possible answers:
   1. Yo voy a ver arte en un museo. 2. Tú vas a ver un cantante en el teatro. 3. Miguel va a estudiar en la biblioteca. 4. Las muchachas van a comer pollo en un restaurante.

9. **For each of the following sentences, choose the verb in parentheses that makes sense and fill in the correct conjugated form in the space. (5 points)**

   1. comprenden 2. Sabe 3. veo 4. haces 5. tomamos

10. **Imagine you are considering taking a job and living in Mexico for a year. Answer the following questions. (10 points)**

   Possible answers include:
   1. - 2. Museums, art galleries, Aztec ruins, parks, art galleries. 3. - 4. Beans, rice, corn. 5. - 6. Answers will vary. 7. Answers will vary. 8. - 10. Answers will vary.

11. **Look at the enlarged section of a map of Mexico City and answer the following questions in complete sentences in Spanish. (10 points)**

1. El Restaurante Olé está en la Calle Veracruz. 2. Se llama Museo de Arte Moderno. 3. El Teatro Real está en la Avenida Robles. 4. No, la Avenida Robles está cerca de la Calle Cisneros. 5. Sí, hay una. Se llama Tienda Mexicana.

12. **Answer the following questions in Spanish in complete sentences. (6 points)**

1. Mañana voy a (*infintive*). 2. Sí, (no, no) leo el periódico. 3. Sí, (no, no) sé dónde hay un restaurante mexicano.

CAPÍTULO 4

Lección 7

Listening Comprehension Test

1. **Look at the sentences that follow as you listen carefully to some descriptions in Spanish. Then circle the letter of the sentence that you hear. (5 points)**

1. Isabel y Lola son unas chicas muy amables.	B
2. Daniela y Mercedes son unas chicas muy divertidas.	A
3. Las dos chicas populares son Amparo y Luisa.	B
4. Mis sobrinos Guillermo y Tomás son muy populares.	A
5. Mis abuelos son muy cariñosos.	B

2. **Listen carefully to the following sentences that describe family relationships. Each sentence will be repeated. Write the letter of the family member that corresponds to what you hear. Not all answer choices are used. (7 points)**

1. Son las hermanas de mi madre.	E
2. Es la esposa de mi abuelo.	A
3. Son las hijas de mi tío.	G
4. Es el esposo de mi tía.	D
5. Es la hija de mi hermano.	H
6. Es el hermano de mi prima.	F
7. Son los padres de mi padre.	B

3. **In the space provided, write the letter of the illustration that best corresponds to each description you hear. (6 points)**

1. Ellos son mis otros abuelos.	C
2. Ellos son primos.	A
3. Mis abuelos son muy simpáticos.	C
4. Mis hermanas son muy populares.	B
5. Ellas son muy divertidas.	B
6. Mis primos son muy guapos.	A

4. **Listen carefully to the following pairs of sentences. They will not be repeated. If the second sentence is a logical response to the first, circle the letter *L.* If it is illogical, circle the letter *I.* (10 points)**

1. ¿Son tus padres en la foto? Sí, ella es mi tía.	I
2. ¿Quiénes son doña Graciela y don Alberto? Ellos son mis tíos.	L
3. ¿Son tus sobrinas de Puerto Rico? Sí, mis sobrinas son de Costa Rica y son inteligentes.	I
4. ¿Son los chicos en la playa tus hermanos? No, ellos no son de Puerto Rico.	I
5. ¿A qué hora vamos a nuestra casa? Vamos a nuestra casa a las ocho.	L
6. ¿Están Héctor y Pepe en casa ahora? No, Héctor y Pepe no están en la playa.	I
7. ¿Es él tu hermano? Sí, es él.	L
8. ¿Son ellos los primos de Gustavo? No, ellos son mis primos.	L
9. ¿Es la chica de Venezuela tu prima? Sí, es mi prima.	L
10. ¿Dónde está nuestra abuela? Ella está en Miami.	L

5. **You will hear a paragraph about a Spanish-speaking family. It will be repeated. You will then hear some statements about the family. Circle the letter *C (cierta)* if a statement is true or *F (falsa)* if it is false. (8 points)**

Yo me llamo Josefina Ramírez. Estoy en Colombia con mis padres. Mis tíos están en Puerto Rico con mis dos primos, Diego y Catalina. Mis abuelos están en Puerto Rico también. Mis padres y yo vamos a Puerto Rico en el verano. Estoy muy contenta porque mi familia es muy amable.

1. Ella se llama Josefina.	C
2. Ella está en México.	F
3. Sus tíos están en Puerto Rico.	C
4. Diego y Catalina son sus sobrinos.	F
5. Ella y sus padres van a Puerto Rico en el verano.	C
6. Ella está con sus abuelos en Colombia.	F
7. Ella está muy contenta.	C
8. San Juan está en Colombia.	F

6. **Listen carefully to some descriptions in Spanish. Then in the space provided, write the letter of the illustration that best corresponds to each description you hear. (8 points)**

1. Está enfermo.	E
2. Está ocupado.	G
3. Ella está muy triste.	C
4. Andrés está contento hoy.	A
5. Alfonso está apurado.	B

6. Pilar está cansada. H
7. Mi hermano es muy loco. F
8. Ana es una chica guapa. D

END OF LISTENING COMPREHENSION TEST

Written Test

7. Create questions in Spanish to ask how various people and things are, using the information given below. Make the necessary changes for verb, noun and adjective agreement. (10 points)

1. ¿Está enferma Bárbara? 2. ¿Está cansada nuestra madre? 3. ¿Están fríos los refrescos? 4. ¿Están nerviosos tus padres? 5. ¿Está limpia la casa?

8. Complete logically the following sentences with the correct present-tense of the verbs *vivir* or *salir*. (8 points)

1. vive 2. vivimos 3. sales 4. salgo 5. viven 6. vives 7. sale 8. salimos

9. Imagine this list of guests is included in a note to a friend you are inviting to a party. Complete the invitation list logically, using one of the words shown. Words may be used more than once. (9 points)

Possible answers:
1. nuestros 2. su 3. mi 4. su 5. sus 6. su 7. sus 8. su 9. tu

10. Write the letter of the word or name in the column on the right that best answers the questions in the column on the left. Each answer choice is used once only. (5 points)

1. B 2. C 3. D 4. A 5. E

11. Complete the dialog between Fernando and his aunt, choosing from the following words: *divertido, qué, apurado, verdad, enfermas, todo, libres, cansada.* (8 points)

1. cansada 2. apurado 3. libres 4. divertido 5. Qué 6. enfermas 7. verdad 8. todo

12. Read the following paragraph. Then give short answers in Spanish to the questions that follow. (6 points)

Possible answers:
1. Se llama Carmen López Herrera. 2. Vive en Miami. 3. Es López. 4. Hay catorce. 5. Están en Puerto Rico y Miami. 6. Sí, está muy ocupada.

13. Answer the following questions in Spanish, using complete sentences. You may make up any information you wish. (10 points)

Possible answers:
1. Sí, estoy triste. No, estoy contento/a. 2. Mi amigo/a favorito/a es amable y divertido/a. 3. Sí, (No, no) tengo *(number)* hermanos. 4. Soy guapo/a y amable. 5. Vivo en (*city*).

CAPÍTULO 4

Lección 8

Listening Comprehension Test

1. **Listen carefully to the following sentences. They will not be repeated. If you hear a form of the verb *ser,* circle the word *ser.* If you hear a form of the verb *estar,* circle the word *estar.* (5 points)**

1. ¿Dónde están Yolanda y Rodrigo?	estar
2. Estamos muy contentas, gracias.	estar
3. Alberto es de Santo Domingo.	ser
4. El concierto es en el parque.	ser
5. Ella es interesante, ¿verdad?	ser

2. **Listen to the following sentences. They will not be repeated. If the second sentence is a logical response to the first, circle the letter *L.* If the sentence is illogical, circle *I.* (8 points)**

1. Chico, ¿te gusta ir de compras?. Sí, no soy alto.	I
2. ¡Qué horrible! Sí, es muy malo.	L
3. ¡Qué dulce eres! Gracias.	L
4. ¡Qué feo! Ella es la chica ideal.	I
5. ¿Cuántos buenos amigos tienes? Tengo muchos.	L
6. ¡Qué cómicos! Sí, y son muy divertidos.	L
7. ¿Es él canoso? Sí, ella tiene un hermano.	I
8. ¡Qué simpática! ¿Verdad? Sí, y es una buena amiga también.	L

3. **You will hear some questions. They will not be repeated. Circle the letter of the logical response for each. (6 points)**

1. ¿Está Carolina siempre con amigos?	B
2. ¿Por qué le gusta a José contestar las preguntas en clase?	A
3. ¿Es Gloria muy dulce?	B
4. ¿Cómo es tu amiga?	A
5. ¿Por qué no te gusta tocar el piano?	B
6. ¿Esteban no es generoso?	A

4. **Listen carefully to some statements about what these people are doing. Write the letter of the illustration that best corresponds to each sentence you hear. (10 points)**

1. Están en la playa.	C
2. A los hermanos de Verónica y Carmen les gusta nadar.	C
3. Enrique va en una bicicleta muy rápida.	B

4. Le gusta tocar el piano. A
5. A la señora le gusta ir de compras. B
6. Les gusta bailar. A
7. Ellas van a oír la radio. C
8. Paloma contesta "sí". C
9. Les gusta jugar al tenis. B
10. Le gusta cantar porque su voz es dulce. A

5. **You will hear six questions. When each question is repeated, write the letter of the most appropriate answer in the space provided. (6 points)**

1. ¿Les gustan a Uds. las bicicletas? A
2. ¿Te gusta mucho la clase de historia? F
3. ¿Les gusta el béisbol? B
4. ¿Les gusta a Uds. nadar mucho? E
5. ¿Qué te gusta hacer mucho? C
6. ¿Te gusta cantar? D

END OF LISTENING COMPREHENSION TEST

Written Test

6. **Circle the verb that logically completes the following sentences. (10 points)**

1. somos 2. son 3. estoy 4. es 5. están 6. es 7. está 8. está 9. son 10. eres

7. **Match the following antonyms (words with an opposite meaning). Write the letter of the matching word in the space provided. (9 points)**

1. H 2. G 3. D 4. I 5. J 6. A 7. C 8. F 9. B

8. **Determine which of the following phrases most logically adds clarity or emphasis to the following sentences: *a mí, a ti, a él, a ella, a ellos,* or *a ellas.* Use the words in parentheses as cues. Write your answer in the space provided. (8 points)**

1. A mí 2. A ellos 3. A él 4. A ellas 5. A ellos 6. A ti 7. A él 8. A mí

9. **Read the following statements about the Dominican Republic. Write the letter *C* if a statement is true or *F* if it is false. (5 points)**

1. C 2. C 3. C 4. F 5. F

10. **Use the appropriate present-tense form of *gustar* to report the results of a survey on what various people like or do not like. (12 points)**

1. A mi mamá le gustan los aviones rápidos. 2. A mi profesor(a) de español le gusta hablar español. 3. A Federico le gusta la música de piano. 4. A ti te gustan los libros interesantes. 5. A mis hermanas les gusta jugar al tenis. 6. A Ramón y a mí nos gusta cantar y bailar.

11. **Read the paragraph about Gregorio Sánchez and his friends. Then answer the questions that follow by circling the letter of the correct response. (5 points)**

1. B 2. C 3. A 4. B 5. C

12. **Complete the paragraph logically, using the words and expressions shown. Each answer choice may be used once only. (10 points)**

1. buena 2. inteligentes 3. cómico 4. jugar 5. cantar 6. inglés 7. ver 8. mirar 9. de compras 10. oír

13. **Answer the following questions in Spanish, using complete sentences. You may make up any information you wish. (6 points)**

Possible answers:
1. Soy alto/a y moreno/a (rubio/a, delgado/a). 2. Sí, (No, no) juego al béisbol en el parque. 3. A mí me gusta nadar, bailar, ver la televisión y oír la radio.

CAPÍTULO 5

Lección 9

Listening Comprehension Test

1. **Listen carefully to the following statements. Then circle the letter of the day of the week when each event is scheduled. (6 points)**

1. Fernando tiene práctica de tenis el martes.	martes
2. El sábado tengo clase de guitarra.	sábado
3. Felipe y su primo hacen un viaje a Costa Rica el viernes.	viernes
4. El miércoles vamos a buscar el nuevo CD.	miércoles
5. Mi compañero juega al fútbol los lunes.	lunes
6. Tú vas a la librería el jueves.	jueves

2. **Listen carefully to the following sentences. They will not be repeated. If the second sentence is a logical response to the first, circle the letter *L*. If it is illogical, circle the letter *I*. (10 points)**

1. Quiero comprar un casete nuevo. Pues, vamos al estadio.	I
2. ¿Tienes discos compactos? Sí, tengo cuarenta.	L
3. ¿Qué discos son populares ahora? Pues, toco la guitarra un poco.	I
4. Vamos a comprar un disco compacto. Me gusta pasar horas en la librería.	I
5. Necesito comprar un disco compacto, pero no tengo dinero. ¡Qué sorpresa! Nunca tienes dinero.	L
6. ¿Por qué no vamos mañana al concierto de rock? No tengo dinero.	L

7. Necesito buscar mi grabadora. I
   Entonces, vamos al concierto.
8. ¿Qué música te gusta? I
   Primero, me gustan los deportes.
9. ¿Compramos un perro? I
   Sí, vamos a la tienda de música.
10. ¿Te gusta la música? L
    Sí, me gustan las canciones de amor.

3. **Listen carefully to several statements in Spanish. Then circle the letter of the exclamation that logically corresponds to what you hear.** (7 points)

1. Vas a un concierto de música fantástica. A
2. Tu canción favorita está en la radio. B
3. Vas a una película muy cómica. A
4. Te gusta el disco compacto nuevo. B
5. No tienes dinero para comprar un estéreo. B
6. Vas a un viaje interesante en Costa Rica. A
7. Tu compañero te compra tres maletas para un viaje. A

4. **You will hear several sentences in Spanish about what people are doing or are going to do. Write the letter of the illustration that best corresponds to each sentence you hear.** (10 points)

1. Yolanda y Ricardo estudian para el examen. B
2. Carlos siempre llama a sus amigos. A
3. Ella canta canciones de amor. A
4. Eduardo quiere a su gato. A
5. Ellos bailan bien. A
6. Es fantástica. ¡Qué canción! B
7. Mis abuelos caminan todos los días. B
8. Ella monta a caballo. B
9. Mi primo toca la guitarra muy bien. A
10. Vamos a oír la música en la grabadora. B

END OF LISTENING COMPREHENSION TEST

Written Test

5. **Look at the illustration and say whether you see the people and objects named.** (9 points)

1. No, no la veo. 2. Sí, los veo. 3. Sí, lo veo. 4. Sí, las veo. 5. Sí, la veo.
6. No, no lo veo. 7. Sí, los veo. 8. No, no las veo. 9. Sí, te veo.

6. **Complete the following sentences with the word *a*, where appropriate, or with an *X* if the word *a* is not required.** (6 points)

1. a 2. a 3. x 4. x 5. x 6. a

7. **Complete the following sentences with the correct present-tense form of the verb *tener* to indicate what everybody at Manolo's party has. (6 points)**

   1. tiene 2. tienen 3. tengo 4. tenemos 5. tiene 6. tienes

8. **Study this schedule for a typical week in the life of Roberto and José. Use the information to complete the sentences that follow. The first one has been done for you. (9 points)**

   1. lunes 2. montan 3. martes 4. práctica 5. estadio 6. fútbol 7. playa
   8. estudian 9. guitarra 10. nadar

9. **Complete these sentences logically with one of the following pronouns: *me, te, le, les* or *nos.* (5 points)**

   1. me 2. te 3. le 4. les 5. nos

10. **Read the question then circle the letter of the more logical response. (5 points)**

    1. A 2. A 3. A 4. B 5. B

11. **Read the following statements about Costa Rica. Write the letter *C* if a statement is true or *F* if it is false. (6 points)**

    1. C 2. F 3. C 4. F 5. C 6. F

12. **Read this paragraph about Nicolás. Then give short answers in Spanish to the questions that follow. (8 points)**

    1. Va el viernes que viene. 2. Es en la casa de Sofía. 3. No/Nunca bailan merengue en las fiestas de Sofía. 4. Sofía no tiene discos de música merengue. 5. Necesita ir a la tienda de música. 6. No le gusta pasar mucho tiempo en las tiendas. 7. Busca dos discos compactos para la fiesta. 8. Va a comprar unas canciones populares de música merengue.

13. **Answer the following questions in Spanish, using complete sentences. You may make up any information you wish. (8 points)**

    Possible answers:
    1. Mi día favorito es sábado porque.... 2. Me gusta pasar mi tiempo libre en....
    3. Sí, compro discos compactos de mi música favorita. 4. Las canciones de...son muy populares ahora.

14. **In Spanish, write at least five statements about a typical week during the school year. Be as specific as you can, naming specific activities, which days during the week you participate in the activities and how you feel about them. You may wish to use some of the following words and expressions in your paragraph: *me gusta, no me gusta, familia, amigos, colegio, biblioteca, estudiar, ir de compras, ver televisión, oír discos compactos, jugar fútbol, escuchar música en el estéreo, ver una película, todos los días, etc.* (5 points)**

    Creative self-expression.

CAPÍTULO 5

Lección 10

Listening Comprehension Test

1. **Listen to the dialog between Gerardo and Alicia. When the dialog is repeated, write the missing words and phrases in the spaces provided. (6 points)**

GERARDO: Alicia, mañana es mi cumpleaños.
ALICIA: ¿De veras? ¿Cuántos años vas a cumplir?
GERARDO: Diecisiete. Tú vienes a mi fiesta, ¿verdad?
ALICIA: ¿Dónde y cuándo es?
GERARDO: Es en casa de mi hermano mayor, a las ocho.
ALICIA: ¡Qué bueno! Necesito salir temprano porque voy en autobús. ¿Está bien?
GERARDO: ¡Sí! Hasta mañana, Alicia.

2. **Imagine you are making a purchase in a Spanish-speaking country where the currency used is *pesos*. Listen as several people say how many pesos they are going to give you in change. When the sentence is repeated, write the number you hear in the space provided. (6 points)**

Modelo: Aquí tiene su cambio, cien pesos, gracias. 100

1. Aquí tiene su cambio, treinta mil seiscientos ochenta pesos, gracias. 30.680
2. Aquí tiene su cambio, doscientos pesos, gracias. 200
3. Aquí tiene su cambio, trescientos quince pesos, gracias. 315
4. Aquí tiene su cambio, mil quinientos pesos, gracias. 1.500
5. Aquí tiene su cambio, tres mil doscientos dos pesos, gracias. 3.202
6. Aquí tiene su cambio, cuatrocientos ochenta y cinco pesos, gracias. 485

3. **Listen to the following sentences. They will be repeated. If the second sentence is a logical response to the first, circle the letter *L*. If it is illogical, circle *I*. (8 points)**

1. Ayer fue el cuatro de julio, ¿no? I
   Sí, y mañana es el tres de julio.
2. Hoy es el treinta y uno de diciembre. ¿Qué fecha es mañana? I
   Es el primero de febrero.
3. Hoy es domingo. ¿Qué día es pasado mañana? L
   Pasado mañana es martes.
4. Hoy es martes, ¿verdad? I
   Sí, y mañana es domingo.
5. Todos los jueves tengo práctica de guitarra. Tengo práctica de guitarra hoy. ¿Qué día es hoy? L
   Hoy es jueves.
6. Hoy es sábado, ¿sí? L
   Pues, sí, y anteayer fue jueves.
7. Ayer fue jueves. ¿Qué día es hoy? I
   Hoy es miércoles.
8. Tu cumpleaños es el diecisiete de julio y hoy es tu cumpleaños. L
   ¿Cuál es la fecha? Es el diecisiete de julio.

4. **You will hear a series of statements about several people's birthdays. The information will be repeated. The second time you hear each statement, circle the letter of the date that corresponds to each date you hear. (6 points)**

1. Mi cumpleaños fue anteayer, el doce de agosto.	B
2. Mi tía nació el primero de octubre de mil novecientos cincuenta y nueve.	B
3. Mi abuela es muy cariñosa, pero es vieja. Ella va a cumplir noventa y ocho años el cuatro de abril.	A
4. Francisco de Goya nació el treinta de marzo de mil setecientos cuarenta y seis.	B
5. Mi papá va a cumplir treinta y cinco años el trece de enero.	A
6. Mi hermana va a cumplir seis años el dieciséis de junio.	B

5. **You will hear some questions about holidays and other special days that occur during the year. The first time you hear the question, look at the clues that follow. When the question is repeated, write your answer to the question in the space provided. Some months may be used more than once. (8 points)**

Modelo: ¿En qué mes es el Día de los Inocentes? diciembre

1. ¿En qué mes es el Día de la Raza?	octubre
2. ¿En qué mes es el día de la Independencia de los Estados Unidos?	julio
3. ¿En qué mes es el Día de San Valentín?	febrero
4. ¿En qué mes es el Día de Año Nuevo?	enero
5. ¿En qué mes es el Día del Trabajo?	mayo
6. ¿En qué mes es el Día de Todos los Santos?	noviembre
7. ¿En qué mes es la Navidad?	diciembre
8. ¿En qué mes es el Día de los Muertos?	noviembre

6. **You will hear a paragraph in Spanish. It will be repeated. Then you will hear statements about the paragraph. Circle the word *sí* if a statement is correct or *no* if it is incorrect. (6 points)**

Hola. Me llamo Rafael. Estamos en marzo y el mes que viene es mi cumpleaños. Voy a cumplir quince años. Pues, sabes que los años pasan rápidamente y pronto voy a tener veintiún años. Voy a ser viejo, y no me gusta la idea ni un poco. Me gusta ser joven.

1. El chico se llama Rafael.	sí
2. El mes que viene, él va a cumplir veintiún años.	no
3. Su cumpleaños es en abril.	sí
4. Los años pasan rápidamente.	sí
5. A él le gusta la idea de ser viejo.	no
6. A él le gusta ser joven.	sí

END OF LISTENING COMPREHENSION TEST

Written Test

7. **Find the pattern and then write the missing numbers in Spanish. (5 points)**

   1. dos mil 2. trescientos 3. siete mil setecientos setenta y siete 4. setecientos cincuenta 5. diez mil

8. **Tell in which month the following events take place, according to the cues. Write the name of each month in Spanish in the space provided. (6 points)**

   1. septiembre 2. enero 3. abril 4. marzo 5. diciembre 6. febrero

9. **Imagine that you are the person in charge of hosting a three-day long archaelogical seminar at Hotel Intercontinental in Managua. Referring to the schedule of the seminar, answer the following questions that the attendees ask you over the telephone. (5 points)**

   1. La gran recepción es el domingo. 2. El seminario es de cuatro días. 3. Vamos a ver los volcanes el martes. 4. No. Vamos a la Costa de los Mosquitos el miércoles. 5. Todos salen del hotel el miércoles, cinco de mayo.

10. **Now imagine that you have to reserve rooms for the people coming to the seminar. With your assistant, review the list of when people will be coming to the seminar, according to the information that follows. Be sure to use the appropriate form of the verb *venir* in each of the provided spaces in order to complete your report. (6 points)**

    1. vienes 2. vengo 3. venimos 4. vienen 5. viene 6. vienen

11. **Read this postcard that Benjamín wrote to his friend Miguel. Then answer the questions that follow by circling the letter of the correct response. (5 points)**

    1. A 2. A 3. B 4. B 5. B

12. **Answer these questions as if today were Thursday, July 31. (9 points)**

    1. Hoy es jueves. 2. Mañana es viernes. 3. Mañana es el primero de agosto. 4. Anteayer fue martes. 5. Ayer fue miércoles. 6. En una semana es jueves. 7. En dos semanas es el catorce de agosto. 8. En treinta y cinco días es septiembre. 9. Estamos en julio.

13. **Complete the following paragraph, using the words shown. Not all answer choices are used. (10 points)**

    1. Querida 2. Sabes 3. pasado 4. cumpleaños 5. cumplir 6. Ciento cincuenta 7. venir 8. Anteayer 9. tienes 10. Feliz

14. **Read the following statements about Nicaragua. Write the letter *C* if a statement is true or *F* if it is false. (8 points)**

    1. F 2. C 3. F 4. C 5. C 6. F 7. C 8. F

15. **Answer the following questions in Spanish, using complete sentences. You may make up any information you wish. (6 points)**

Possible answers:
1. Tengo *(number of years)* años. 2. Mi cumpleaños es *(day/month).* 3. Voy a cumplir veintiún años en *(date or number of years).*

ACHIEVEMENT TEST I

Listening Comprehension Test

1. **Imagine you overhear one person dicussing another. Could you tell whether the person being discussed is male or a female? Listen carefully to several statements. They will not be repeated. If a statement refers to a male, circle *M* (for masculine). If the statement refers to a female, circle *F* (for feminine). (4 points)**

1. Es una estudiante nueva de Nicaragua.	F
2. La chica alta es mi hermana.	F
3. No lo veo.	M
4. El muchacho moreno es de Colombia.	M

2. **Listen to the dialog between Marisol and Sara. When the dialog is repeated, write the missing words in the spaces provided. (10 points)**

MARISOL: Hola, Sara.
SARA: Marisol, ¿qué tal?
MARISOL: Muy bien, Sara. Cumplo dieciséis años hoy y estoy muy feliz.
SARA: ¿De veras? ¡Qué fantástico!
MARISOL: Verdad, ¿no?
SARA: ¡Claro! Pues, ¡feliz cumpleaños, Marisol!
MARISOL: Gracias, Sara. Mira, busco a mi prima, Paula. ¿La ves?
SARA: No, no la veo.
MARISOL: Bueno, necesito ir a buscar a Paula. Adiós, Sara.
SARA: Hasta luego, Marisol.

3. **Listen carefully to the following greetings and farewells. Then circle the letter of the more appropriate response for each. (5 points)**

1. ¿Cómo estás, Rosario?	B
2. Buenas noches, Sr. Molina.	A
3. ¡Hola! ¿Cómo están Uds.?	B
4. Hola, Diego. ¿Qué tal?	A
5. Buenos días, Sra. López.	A

4. **Listen carefully to some sentences in Spanish that include the names of several people. If you hear a boy's name, circle the word *muchacho*. If you hear a girl's name, circle the word *muchacha*.** (4 points)

1. ¿Cómo se escribe Javier? — muchacho
2. ¿Dónde está Rosa? — muchacha
3. Adiós, Patricia. — muchacha
4. Buenos días, Manuel. — muchacho

5. **Listen carefully to the following sentences. They will not be repeated. If the second sentence is a logical response to the first, circle the letter *L*. If it is illogical, circle *I*.** (6 points)

1. ¿Qué hora es? — L
   Son las diez menos cinco.
2. ¡Mucho gusto! — L
   Encantada.
3. ¿En qué página estamos? — I
   No es mi regla.
4. ¿Cuántas pizarras hay? — I
   No tengo mi cuaderno aquí.
5. ¿Cuándo es tu clase de matemáticas? — I
   La profesora de biología es la señora Giraldo.
6. ¿Cómo se dice *teacher?* — I
   Se dice "estudiante".

6. **You will hear several statements about several people's schedules. When each sentence is repeated, write the letter of the clock that represents the time you hear for each statement.** (5 points)

1. Mi clase de español fue al medio día. — E
2. Blanca va al dentista a las tres y media. — B
3. Carlos va a su clase de biología a las diez. — C
4. Mis tíos vienen a mi casa a las cinco menos cuatro. — A
5. Ellos van a su casa a las cuatro menos cuarto. — D

7. **Listen carefully to some statements about various people. Circle the letter of the subject pronoun that matches the verb form for each sentence you hear.** (6 points)

1. Josefina, Ramón y Maribel quieren ir al museo. — B
2. Eres de Venezuela, ¿verdad? — A
3. Tú y yo somos delgados, ¿verdad? — B
4. Sr. Córdoba, Ud. toca el piano muy bien. — A
5. Carmen, Elena y Teresa van al centro a las siete. — A
6. Mi hermano mayor está en la oficina. — A

8. **You will hear several statements in Spanish. They will not be repeated. Circle the letter *C* if a statement is true or *F* if it is false.** (10 points)

1. Hablan español en Costa Rica, Nicaragua y Puerto Rico. — C
2. La capital de la República Dominicana es Santo Domingo. — C
3. La capital de Costa Rica es San Juan. — F
4. Juan Ponce de León fue el primer gobernador de Puerto Rico. — C

5. Costa Rica está en la isla de La Española. F
6. Hay volcanes en Costa Rica y en Nicaragua. C
7. Hay dos lagos grandes en Nicaragua: el lago Managua y el lago Nicaragua. C
8. El D.F. es la capital de México. C
9. Hay ruinas arqueológicas aztecas en México. C
10. Ponce es la capital de Puerto Rico. F

9. Listen as the following people leave a telephone message consisting of their name and number. You will hear each message twice. When each message is repeated, fill in the blank space with the number you hear. (5 points)

Modelo: Soy Esteban del Mar y mi número de teléfono es el 2-<u>26</u>-30-95.

1. Soy Alfonso Trujillo y mi número de teléfono es el 6-23-<u>14</u>-92.
2. Soy Federico Guerra y mi número de teléfono es el 3-55-<u>61</u>-71.
3. Soy la Dra. Herrera y mi número de teléfono es el 5-<u>39</u>-54-37.
4. Soy Paz Gaviria y mi número de teléfono es el 2-63-08-<u>14</u>.
5. Soy Arturo Segovia y mi número de teléfono es el 5-<u>68</u>-31-44.

10. Listen carefully to the following questions. Then circle the letter of the more logical response for each. (6 points)

1. ¿De dónde son Uds.? A
2. ¿Eres tú amigo de Roberto? B
3. ¿Cómo es la amiga de David? B
4. ¿Cuál es tu número de teléfono? A
5. ¿De quién es el libro de español? A
6. ¿De dónde eres tú? A

11. You will hear several dates. Each one will be repeated. Circle the letter of the response that is the same as the date you hear. (5 points)

1. Fue el dieciséis de junio de mil novecientos ochenta y seis. B
2. Fue el quince de mayo de mil ochocientos sesenta y ocho. B
3. Fue el catorce de febrero de mil novecientos cuarenta y ocho. A
4. Fue el veinticinco de diciembre de mil setecientos setenta y siete. B
5. Fue el doce de julio de mil quinientos cincuenta y cinco. A

12. You will hear two brief paragraphs, followed by questions. Listen carefully, the information will not be repeated. Circle the letter of the most appropriate response for each each question. (8 points)

Me llamo Gabriela Guevara. Tengo quince años. Vivo en San Juan, Puerto Rico, con mis padres y mi hermano Timoteo. En el verano vamos a Miami.

1. ¿Cómo se llama ella? B
2. ¿Cuántos hermanos tiene? C
3. ¿Dónde vive ella y su familia? B
4. ¿Adónde van ellos en el verano? B

Soy Marta. Mañana es mi cumpleaños. Voy a cumplir dieciséis años. Mis padres van a tener una fiesta muy grande mañana a las siete en mi casa. Todos mis amigos vienen. Tengo ocho casetes nuevos y vamos a bailar toda la noche.

5. ¿Cuántos años va a cumplir ella?	C
6. ¿Cuándo es la fiesta?	A
7. ¿Dónde es la fiesta?	A
8. ¿Cuántos casetes tiene Marta?	A

END OF LISTENING COMPREHENSION TEST

Written Test

13. Complete the following sentences with the following words or groups of words: *del, de la, los, al, a las.* (4 points)

1. a las 2. del 3. de la 4. al

14. Decide whether or not the following sentences need the personal *a.* You must also decide whether they need the definite article and make any necessary contractions. If nothing is needed, write an *X* in the space provided. (4 points)

1. a 2. x 3. al 4. a la

15. Circle the word or expression that most logically does not belong in each of the following groups of three. (10 points)

1. estéreo 2. carro 3. Hola. 4. apellido 5. a veces 6. luz 7. tiza 8. caballo 9. siempre 10. Nicaragua

16. Find the antonyms (words with an opposite meaning) for the italicized words in the column on the right. Then write the letter of that word in the space provided. Some answer choices may not be used. (6 points)

1. A 2. E 3. D 4. C 5. F 6. H

17. Ask whether the people named like the following, according to the cues. Be sure to use the appropriate present-tense forms of *gustar* in your question. (10 points)

1. ¿Te gusta ir de compras? 2. ¿A tus padres les gustan los deportes? 3. ¿A Uds. les gusta mucho el teatro? 4. ¿Al señor Saavedra le gustan los museos? 5. ¿A tus hermanos les gusta montar a caballo?

18. Write the correct present-tense form of the indicated verbs to create a logical statement about the following people. (15 points)

1. vivimos 2. estoy 3. hablamos 4. vienen 5. necesito 6. presento 7. vas 8. tengo 9. haces 10. salgo 11. salen 12. come 13. ven 14. estudia 15. hago

19. **Complete the following questions with the appropriate present-tense form of the verb *ser* or *estar* in order to find out as much as you can about various people. (5 points)**

1. Son 2. Están 3. están 4. es 5. es

20. **Look at this invitation list for an imaginary family gathering. Then choose from the following possessive adjectives to complete the list logically: *mi/mis, tu/tus, su/sus, nuestro/nuestros, nuestra/nuestras.* (6 points)**

1. mis 2. tus 3. nuestras 4. sus 5. sus 6. su

21. **Indicate where the following people are going and how they are getting there by combining the following words. Be sure to add extra words as needed and to include the correct form of the verb *ir.* (10 points)**

1. Yo voy al centro en autobús. 2. Mario y Rebeca van a la biblioteca en bicicleta. 3. Nosotros vamos a la playa a caballo. 4. Tú vas al cine a pie. 5. Mi mamá va a Venezuela en avión.

22. **Look at the following descriptions of family relationships. In the space provided, write the letter of the family member that corresponds to each description. Not all answer choices are used. (6 points)**

1. C 2. B 3. A 4. E 5. D 6. G

23. **Carmen always has to have the last word. Complete her statements by saying that the following people or items are not like the ones previously mentioned. Make any necessary changes in verb form and in the number and gender of the adjectives and nouns. Follow the model. (10 points)**

1. no están cerradas 2. no son muy populares 3. no es canosa 4. no está aburrido 5. no es cariñosa

24. **Complete the following sentences with the appropriate Spanish question-asking words. (5 points)**

Possible answers:
1. Dónde 2. Adónde 3. Cuándo 4. Por qué 5. Cómo

25. **In the space provided, write the correct masculine or feminine definite article *(el* or *la)* for each of the following words. (4 points)**

1. la 2. la 3. el 4. el

26. **Imagine today is Monday. Then give a one-word answer to the following questions. (4 points)**

1. Anteayer fue sábado. 2. Pasado mañana es miércoles. 3. Ayer fue domingo. 4. Mañana es martes.

27. **Read the following statements. Write the letter *C* if a statement is true or *F* if it is false. (6 points)**

 1. C 2. C 3. C 4. F 5. F 6. F

28. **Look at the picture and then answer the questions that follow affirmatively or negatively, using direct object pronouns. (5 points)**

 1. Sí, las veo. 2. Sí, los veo. 3. No, no los veo. 4. Sí, la veo. 5. No, no lo veo.

29. **Complete the following paragraph logically with phrases from the box. Not all answer choices are used. (6 points)**

 1. los Estados Unidos 2. la ciudad 3. cerca de 4. grandes 5. nos gusta 6. hay

30. **Describe each of the following pictures with at least five complete sentences in Spanish. Use as much vocabulary as possible. Be sure to use the correct verb forms, and check to see that the nouns and adjectives agree in number and gender. (10 points)**

 Creative self-expression.

CAPÍTULO 6

Lección 11

Listening Comprehension Test

1. **Listen carefully to the following phrases. Circle the word *debo* if what you hear refers to something you should do; circle *tengo que* for each phrase that refers to a task you have to do. (5 points)**

1.	tomar ocho vasos de agua todos los días	debo
2.	comer todos los días	tengo que
3.	poner poca sal a la comida	debo
4.	encender la luz cuando son las diez de la noche	tengo que
5.	ser generoso con los amigos	debo

2. **Listen carefully to the following sentences. They will not be repeated. If the sentence is logical, circle the letter *L*. If it is illogical, circle *I*. (10 points)**

1.	El lavaplatos está en la cocina.	L
2.	Comemos primero el postre, después la sopa.	I
3.	Mario toma la sopa con un cuchillo.	I
4.	Cuando pongo la mesa, primero necesito el mantel.	L
5.	Pásame la luz, por favor.	I
6.	Yo como agua mineral con una cucharita.	I
7.	Me gusta comer pan con mantequilla.	L
8.	Yo viajo a Caracas.	L
9.	Después de comer, ellos ponen la mesa en el refrigerador.	I
10.	Yo pongo la sal en el fregadero.	I

3. **Listen carefully to the following sentences. If a sentence contains an object that is normally found in a kitchen or dining room, circle the word *sí.* If the sentence mentions something that is not usually associated with kitchens or dining rooms, circle the word *no.* (10 points)**

1. La sal y la pimienta están en la mesa, ¿verdad? sí
2. Nuestra bicicleta está en la calle. no
3. Esta lámpara es muy bonita. no
4. Estos manteles son muy especiales. sí
5. Los platos de sopa están en el fregadero. sí
6. Yo leo el periódico en el autobús. no
7. Mi mamá va a cerrar el carro. no
8. En mi cuarto tengo un estéreo y una computadora. no
9. Tenemos una estufa grande. sí
10. ¿Qué piensas de nuestro lavaplatos nuevo? sí

4. **Imagine you are shopping for some of the items in this illustration. Listen as the sales person asks several questions. Each question will be repeated. In the space provided, write the letter that identifies where the objects mentioned are located. (8 points)**

1. ¿Quiere Ud. mirar estos vasos? B
2. ¿Prefiere Ud. ver esos vasos? F
3. ¿Quiere Ud. ver aquellos cubiertos? I
4. ¿Quiere Ud. ver estos cubiertos primero? A
5. ¿Quiere Ud. ver aquellos platos? K
6. ¿Prefiere Ud. ver esos platos también? G
7. Ud. quiere comprar estas tazas, ¿verdad? D
8. ¿Va a comprar Ud. estos platos también? C

5. **You will now hear several people talk about themselves, followed by statements about what each person has said. Listen carefully. The information will not be repeated. Circle the letter *C* if a statement is true or *F* if it is false. (10 points)**

Me llamo Verónica. Pienso hacer un postre especial para mi familia. Necesito comprar mantequilla y aceite. Ya tengo un poquito de azúcar y todas las otras cosas que necesito para hacer el postre.

1. Verónica ya tiene mantequilla y aceite. F
2. Tiene que comprar aceite. C

Me llamo Santiago. Pienso ir al cine con mis primos. Debo estudiar, pero no quiero. ¿Qué debo hacer? Pues, voy a estudiar.

3. Santiago piensa ir al centro. F
4. Santiago quiere estudiar. F
5. Él va al cine. F

Me llamo Tomás. Voy a la cocina cuando quiero comer. Quiero comer ahora. ¿Sabes adónde voy? ¿Qué hay en el refrigerador? Ah, pues, voy a comer un poco de esta ensalada.

6. Tomás va a la cocina cuando quiere leer. F
7. Él quiere comer ahora y va a la cocina. C

Me llamo Carmen Vega. Vivo con mi familia en la capital de Venezuela, Caracas. Tengo una casa muy bonita y estoy muy contenta.

8. Carmen vive en Venezuela. C
9. La capital de Venezuela es Carmen. F
10. Carmen tiene una casa fea. F

END OF LISTENING COMPREHENSION TEST

Written Test

6. Complete the following statements by filling in the space provided with one of the following words: *en, de, que*. If nothing is needed, place an *X* in the space. (5 points)

1. en 2. x 3. de 4. que 5. en

7. Fill in the blanks with the appropriate present-tense form of the verb indicated in each sentence. (10 points)

1. prefiere 2. Piensas 3. siente 4. pongo 5. encendemos 6. cierras 7. empiezan 8. ayudan 9. siento 10. queremos

8. Complete the following sentences with the appropriate form of the demonstrative adjective in parentheses. (8 points)

1. Esta 2. esa 3. aquella 4. aquellos 5. esos 6. ese 7. Estos 8. estas

9. Write the Spanish word for the each numbered item. (10 points)

1. plato 2. cuchara 3. tenedor 4. cuchillo 5. servilleta 6. vaso 7. taza 8. postre 9. sal 10. pimienta

10. Circle the letter of the correct response for each of the following questions about Venezuela. (9 points)

1. B 2. B 3. B 4. A 5. A 6. B 7. A 8. B 9. A

11. Read carefully the following dialog between Cristina and Rodrigo. Then give short answers in Spanish to the questions that follow. (8 points)

1. Quiere ayudar a Cristina. 2. Hacen el postre para su abuela. 3. Necesitan el azúcar, la mantequilla, el aceite y un poco de agua. 4. Debe estar en el refrigerador. 5.Quiere la cuchara grande. 6. Está al lado del lavaplatos. 7. Van a hacer otro postre para el cumpleaños de su mamá. 8. Hacen el postre en la cocina.

12. **Imagine that you live in Caracas, Venezuela and that you are planning a dinner party for some friends visiting from the United States. In Spanish, write a composition to describe the party. Include the following in your composition. (7 points)**

    Creative self-expression.

CAPÍTULO 6

Lección 12

Listening Comprehension Test

1. **Listen to some sentences taken from a letter that Jorge wrote to his parents. When the sentences are repeated, write the missing words in the spaces provided. (5 points)**

    1. Estamos aquí en Cartagena desde el jueves.
    2. Esta ciudad es muy bonita e interesante.
    3. Dicen que vamos a pasar siete u ocho días en Bucaramanga.
    4. La casa del primo Martín es grande y cómoda.
    5. Me gustaría estar con Uds. en Caracas.

2. **Listen carefully to the following sentences. They will not be repeated. If the second sentence is a logical response to the first, circle the letter *L.* If it is illogical, circle *I.* (6 points)**

    1. ¿Tienes hambre? — I
       Si, debo ir al baño.
    2. ¿Tienes ganas de ir a Cartagena? — I
       No, no tengo prisa.
    3. Mi casa tiene dos pisos. — L
       Tiene una escalera.
    4. Quiero aprender a montar a caballo. — L
       Debes tomar clases.
    5. ¿Tienes sueño? — I
       Sí, me gustaría repetir un poco de ensalada.
    6. ¿Tienes ganas de correr? — L
       No, estoy cansado.

3. **You will hear several sentences. Listen carefully, they will not be repeated. Based upon what you hear, circle the letter of the response that indicates where these people need to go in the house. (10 points)**

    1. Mis primos vienen a comer por la noche. — B
    2. Mi mamá necesita su carro. — A
    3. Él y yo tenemos hambre. — B
    4. Enrique está cansado. — B
    5. Andrés viene de la práctica de béisbol y tiene calor. — A
    6. Mi abuela tiene sed. — B
    7. Pepito está sucio. — A

8. Mario come a las dos. A
9. Ellos comen con toda la familia los domingos. B
10. Quiero ver la televisión. B

4. **You will hear several sentences in Spanish. Write the letter of the illustration that best represents each sentence you hear. (10 points)**

1. El refrigerador está al lado de la estufa. B
2. Vamos a tomar un refresco en el patio. D
3. Hay una escalera aquí, ¿verdad? A
4. Mi padre lee el periódico en la sala. A
5. Quiero estudiar en mi cuarto ahora. C
6. La sala de mi casa es muy cómoda. A
7. Por la noche escribo en la computadora. C
8. Tenemos una piscina grande. D
9. Tengo hambre. B
10. Me gustaría mirar la televisión. A

5. **Listen carefully to the following sentences. They will not be repeated. Then circle the letter of the most logical conclusion to each one. (5 points)**

1. Jorge no tiene diez dólares para ir al cine. B
2. No sé dónde está el baño en el restaurante. A
3. María quiere ir al concierto de Enrique Iglesias con un amigo. B
4. Nosotros no comprendemos la lección de español. A
5. Carlos y Ana no saben dónde está la piscina. A

END OF LISTENING COMPREHENSION TEST

Written Test

6. **Use the appropriate present-tense form of *decir* and *que* to summarize what the following people are saying. Make sure to make all necessary changes to complete each sentence logically. (5 points)**

1. Dice que siempre come en la cocina por la noche. 2. Dicen que corren cinco días a la semana. 3. Dice que aprende a montar caballo en Cartagena. 4. Dices que mañana haces un dibujo para nosotros. 5. Decimos que nunca repetimos lo que decimos.

7. **Complete the following paragraph with the correct present-tense form of the verbs in parentheses. (8 points)**

1. digo 2. digo 3. repiten 4. debemos 5. pide 6. dice 7. pido 8. digan

8. **Match the sentences in the column on the right with the most logical sentence in the column on the left. Write the letter in the space provided. (10 points)**

1. J 2. A 3. D 4. C 5. E 6. B 7. G 8. H 9. F 10. I

9. **Some people in Santa Fe de Bogota are looking classified advertisements for houses and apartments in a newspaper. Read carefully the following classified advertisements. Then write the letter of the advertisement that each one should call according to their needs. (6 points)**

   Possible answers:
   1. D 2. C 3. A 4. A 5. B 6. C

10. **Read the following paragraph about Diana Tovar. Then answer the questions that follow by circling the letter of the correct response. (10 points)**

    1. B 2. A 3. B 4. B 5. B 6. A 7. A 8. B 9. B 10. B

11. **Complete this dialog between José and Rosa, using the words shown. Not all answer choices are used. (8 points)**

    1. ciudad 2. gustaría 3. vivir 4. pisos 5. pequeño 6. al lado 7. primer
    8. tienes que

12. **Read the following statements about Colombia. Write the letter *C* if a statement is true or *F* if it is false. (7 points)**

    1. C 2. F 3. C 4. C 5. F 6. C 7. F

13. **Write a paragraph in Spanish consisting of at least five complete sentences in which you describe your dream house *(la casa ideal)*. Include the number of rooms, bedrooms, bathrooms and the number of floors. Include any special features you wish, such as a pool, a patio or a garage, for example. (10 points)**

    Creative self-expression.

CAPÍTULO 7

Lección 13

Listening Comprehension Test

1. **Listen to the following sentences. They will not be repeated. If the second sentence is a logical response to the first, circle the letter *L*. If the sentence is illogical, circle *I*. (6 points)**

   1. ¿Puedes ir ahora mismo? — L
      Pues, sí. ¡Vamos!
   2. ¿Cuánto cuesta el televisor? — I
      Me das uno de cumpleaños.
   3. ¿Qué están haciendo Uds.? — I
      Hace un siglo.
   4. ¿A qué hora es mi telenovela? — L
      No sé, pero puedes ver la lista de los programas que está allí.
   5. ¿Cuánto tiempo hace que no duermes? — L
      Hace dos días que no duermo.
   6. ¿Me puedes dar la lista? — I
      Sí, te doy un minuto.

2. **Listen carefully to the following sentences. If a sentence refers to a past event, circle the word *pasado;* if a sentence mentions something that is occurring right now, circle the word *presente;* if a sentence names an activity that is going to occur later, circle the word *futuro.* (8 points)**

1. ¿Qué está dibujando Liliana?	presente
2. El partido de fútbol americano entre Texas y Nueva York fue ayer por la tarde.	pasado
3. Miami y Los Ángeles juegan en dos semanas.	futuro
4. ¿Están apagando las luces?	presente
5. Hace media hora que veo televisión.	presente
6. Guillermo está poniendo el televisor y yo estoy terminando mi tarea.	presente
7. En dos minutos voy a jugar ajedrez con mi amigo, Arturo.	futuro
8. Ese programa fue ayer por la mañana.	pasado

3. **Listen carefully to the following short monologs. After each monolog you will hear two statements about what you heard. Circle the letter *C* if a statement is true or *F* if it is false. (10 points)**

A las siete de la mañana, de lunes a viernes, hay un programa de aeróbicos en la televisión. Me gusta hacer los aeróbicos temprano, porque por la tarde prefiero ver mi telenovela *Vidas nuevas*.

1. El programa de aeróbicos es a las siete de la mañana.	C
2. La telenovela es por la mañana.	F

Hace una semana que no veo mi telenovela favorita a las tres de la tarde. A mi papá le gusta ver un programa de deportes a las tres. Si puedo, voy a ver el programa hoy.

3. Hace cuatro semanas que no ve su telenovela favorita.	F
4. La telenovela es a las tres.	C

Hace media hora que estoy buscando el control remoto porque quiero poner el televisor y todavía no lo veo. Casi son las tres y hay un partido de fútbol estupendo.

5. Está buscando el televisor.	F
6. El partido empieza a las tres.	C

Estoy alquilando una película para ver esta noche. Hay muchas nuevas. Casi todas son buenas pero no puedo alquilar todas las películas. ¡Qué problema! Bueno, voy a alquilar una buena de Argentina.

7. Va a alquilar muchas películas.	F
8. Va a ver una película por la tarde.	F

Hace muchos años que no tengo un televisor. Ahora mismo voy a comprar un televisor muy grande. Quiero ver los partidos de fútbol y básquetbol esta semana.

9. Va a comprar el televisor mañana.	F
10. Quiero ver los partidos de básquetbol y fútbol esta semana.	C

4. **Listen carefully to several statements in Spanish. Then in the space provided, write the letter of the illustration that best corresponds to each sentence you hear. (6 points)**

1. Esos chicos están jugando al volibol. B
2. Hace dos horas que los muchachos están en el parque. B
3. Son las ocho y Pilar y su papá están tomando refrescos. A
4. Están jugando al básquetbol. B
5. Hace veinte minutos que ellos comen. A
6. Hace quince años que mis abuelos viven en mi casa. A

5. **Listen carefully as Alejandro Bernal tells about his favorite pastime. Then answer the questions that follow by circling the letter of the most logical response. (5 points)**

Me llamo Alejandro Bernal. Mi pasatiempo favorito es jugar a las maquinitas. Todos los viernes por la tarde voy con mis amigos a Uniplay donde jugamos por dos horas. Hace un año que jugamos allí.

1. ¿Cuál es el pasatiempo favorito de Alejandro? A
2. ¿Qué días juegan ellos? C
3. ¿Cuántas horas juegan? B
4. ¿Dónde juegan? C
5. ¿Cuánto tiempo hace que juegan allí? B

END OF LISTENING COMPREHENSION TEST

Written Test

6. **Complete each question with the correct present-tense form of the verb in parentheses. (8 points)**

1. recuerdo 2. apagas 3. dibuja 4. Duerme 5. pueden 6. Juegas 7. cuesta 8. vuelves

7. **In the space provided, write the letter of the time expression shown in the column on the right that equals the amount of time shown in the column on the left. Some answer choices may not be used. (5 points)**

1. B 2. E 3. C 4. D 5. A

8. **Ask questions to find out how long these people have been doing the indicated activity, according to the cues. (8 points)**

1. ¿Cuánto tiempo hace que tus hermanas juegan a las damas? 2. ¿Cuánto tiempo hace que (tú) dibujas? 3. ¿Cuánto tiempo hace que (Gregorio) duerme? 4. ¿Cuánto tiempo hace que (nosotros) hacemos aeróbicos?

9. **Answer the following questions, using direct object pronouns and the cues shown. Follow the model. (6 points)**

1. Sí, estoy viéndola. 2. Sí, estoy poniéndolo. 3. No, no estoy dibujándolas. 4. No, no voy a alquilarla. 5. Sí, voy a recordarlo. 6. No, no voy a comprarlas.

10. **Use the present progressive tense to write sentences about imaginary activities you and people you know are doing right now, according to the cues. (12 points)**

1. Yo estoy escribiendo. 2. Ud. está leyendo la lista. 3. Mis padres están viniendo por avión. 4. Tú estás dibujando en la playa. 5. Álvaro está durmiendo. 6. Ellos están jugando a las maquinitas.

11. **Find the indicated items on this map of Argentina and surrounding countries. In the space provided, write the letter that identifies each point of interest. Note that not all sites on the map are used. (8 points)**

1. F 2. I 3. B 4. D 5. C 6. J 7. E 8. L

12. **Read the dialog about Celia and Beto. Then answer the questions that follow in Spanish, using complete sentences. (10 points)**

Possible answers:
1. Ellos están en la sala de la casa de Beto. 2. La amiga de Celia está cumpliendo años. 3. Beto está viendo un partido de fútbol. 4. Después del partido del fútbol la hermana de Beto va a ver su telenovela favorita. 5. Está sobre el televisor.

13. **Write a paragraph in Spanish of at least four sentences about your favorite leisure time activity. The following questions will serve as a guide to help you get started. (8 points)**

Creative self-expression.

CAPÍTULO 7

Lección 14

Listening Comprehension Test

1. **You will hear a series of questions and answers in Spanish. Listen carefully because these mini-dialogs will not be repeated. If the answer you hear for each question is logical, circle the letter *L*. If it is illogical, circle *I*. (7 points)**

1. ¿Eres deportista? — L
   Sí, soy basquetbolista.
2. ¿Cómo es el otoño aquí? — L
   Hace fresco y hace mucho viento.
3. ¿A qué hora sales de la escuela? — I
   Doy un paseo por el parque.
4. ¿Va a nevar? — L
   Ya está nevando.

5. ¿Qué tiempo hace? — I
   Salen con sus amigas el viernes a las cinco.
6. ¿Qué temperatura hace? — L
   Hace casi veinte grados.
7. ¿Hace mucho frío? — L
   ¡Claro! Hace cero grados.

2. Imagine you are talking about the weather with someone from Minnesota. Listen carefully as the person tells what he does and does not like about each of the seasons where he lives. For each statement you hear, circle the season the person is describing. (7 points)

1. Es mi estación favorita porque hace fresco pero no me gusta porque siempre está nublado, especialmente en noviembre. — el otoño
2. Me gusta esta estación porque hace sol, casi nunca llueve y vamos mucho a la playa. — el verano
3. Me gusta esta estación porque hay muchas flores por todos lados pero no me gusta la estación porque llueve mucho. — la primavera
4. Me gusta esta estación porque hace mucho calor y puedo nadar en uno de los diez mil lagos de Minnesota. — el verano
5. En esta estación hace mucho sol y me gusta nadar en la playa cuando hace buen tiempo. — el verano
6. No es mi estación favorita porque hace mucho frío y nieva. — el invierno
7. Me gusta esta estación porque soy esquiador y puedo patinar sobre hielo y esquiar en la nieve. — el invierno

3. Listen carefully to several statements and questions in Spanish. Then in the space provided, write the letter of the illustration that best corresponds to each sentence you hear. (8 points)

1. ¿Dan Uds. un paseo por la playa? — B
2. Hace frío y la temperatura es ideal para esquiar o para patinar sobre hielo. — D
3. ¿Les gusta la playa cuando hace ochenta grados? — B
4. Está lloviendo. — A
5. Salimos a patinar cuando hace fresco en el otoño. — C
6. Hace dos horas que no está nevando. — D
7. Soy futbolista pero me gustan otros deportes del otoño también. — C
8. Está nublado y llueve. — A

4. You will hear some questions about leisure-time activities. They will not be repeated. Circle the letter of the logical response for each. (5 points)

1. ¿Qué haces cuando no puedes correr? — A
2. ¿Qué te gusta hacer en el invierno? — B
3. ¿Dónde es la competencia? — B
4. ¿Qué haces cuando quieres ver televisión? — B
5. ¿A qué hora sales a patinar? — A

5. **Listen carefully to several short paragraphs. After each paragraph you will hear two statements about what you heard. Circle the letter *C* if a statement is true or *F* if it is false. (8 points)**

Me llamo Isabel. Soy corredora. Soy la primera en terminar en la competencia de hoy. Mis amigas están corriendo todavía. Pues, aquí viene Carmen, ella es la segunda en terminar, y allí viene Marisol. Ella va a ser la tercera en terminar.

1. Isabel es tenista. F
2. Marisol va a ser la tercera en terminar en la competencia. C

Hace dos horas que está lloviendo. Estoy mirando la televisión pero no me gusta. No hay programas interesantes. Pienso en salir a jugar al básquetbol.

3. Hace cuatro horas que está nevando. F
4. No hay programas interesantes. C

Guillermo y Tomás son hermanos y buenos deportistas pero son muy diferentes. A Guillermo le gusta mucho el básquetbol, el fútbol y el béisbol. En cambio, Tomás prefiere nadar, montar a caballo y montar en bicicleta.

5. Los dos muchachos son hermanos. C
6. Los dos son patinadores. F

Me llamo Mónica. Estoy esquiando en Portillo, Chile. Hace mucho frío pero es excelente para esquiar o patinar sobre hielo. Está nevando ahora mismo.

7. Es invierno en Portillo. C
8. La nieve y el frío son excelentes para correr y nadar. F

6. **Listen carefully as Gerardo Salas tells about his favorite pastime. Then answer the questions that follow by circling the letter of the more logical response. (7 points)**

Me llamo Gerardo Salas y vivo en Chile. Soy deportista. El fútbol es mi deporte favorito pero también me gusta montar en bicicleta y correr cuando no hace mal tiempo. En cambio, cuando hace frío o nieva en agosto, esquío o patino sobre hielo. Este fin de semana voy a Portillo. No está muy lejos y es un lugar excelente para esquiar.

1. ¿Qué es Gerardo? B
2. ¿Qué deporte le gusta mucho a Gerardo? B
3. ¿Qué hace Gerardo cuando no hace mal tiempo? A
4. ¿Qué hace Gerardo cuando hace frío? A
5. ¿En qué mes va Gerardo a esquiar o a patinar? B
6. ¿Está lejos el lugar donde él va a esquiar? A
7. Si el invierno es en julio en Chile, ¿cuándo es el verano? A

END OF LISTENING COMPREHENSION TEST

Written Test

7. **Complete these sentences with the appropriate present-tense form of the verb *continuar*. Be sure to include the written accent when necessary. (5 points)**

   1. continúa 2. continúan 3. continuamos 4. continúo 5. continúa

8. **Fill in the blanks with the appropriate present-tense form of the indicated verb. (10 points)**

   1. doy 2. ponemos 3. ponen 4. envías 5. Llueve 6. nieva 7. copia 8. esquías 9. esquiamos 10. enviamos

9. **Indicate the order of the top ten cyclists *(ciclistas)* in the co-ed ten kilometer race by completing the sentences with the ordinal place numbers for each sentence. (10 points)**

   1. cuarta 2. tercero 3. sexto 4. décima 5. séptimo 6. novena 7. segundo 8. quinta 9. octavo 10. primera

10. **Mark lives in the United States and wants to know what the weather is like in Chile in July, where his key pal, Alberto, lives. Read the following weather map and forecast for Chile that he found on the Internet. Then answer the questions that follow by circling the letter of the correct response. (5 points)**

    1. A 2. B 3. A 4. B 5. A

11. **Read the following paragraph. Then answer the questions that follow in Spanish. (10 points)**

    Possible answers:
    1. Vive en el sexto piso de un edificio en Santiago, la capital de Chile. 2. Juegan al béisbol y al tenis, montan en bicicleta y dan paseos por las calles de la capital. 3. Su estación favorita es el verano porque hace mucho calor y casi siempre está soleado. 4. Juegan al fútbol y al básquetbol. 5. Van a Portillo en el invierno porque nieva mucho y es perfecto para esquiar.

12. **Read the following statements about Chile. Write the letter *C* if a statement is true or *F* if it is false. (8 points)**

    1. F 2. F 3. F 4. C 5. C 6. C 7. C 8. F

13. **Write one or two paragraphs in Spanish of at least five complete sentences about your favorite season. You must include the following information in your composition. (10 points)**

    Creative self-expression.

CAPÍTULO 8

Lección 15

Listening Comprehension Test

1. **Listen carefully to the following sentences. If a sentence refers to a past event, circle the word *pasado*; if a sentence mentions something that this is occurring right now, circle the word *presente*. (6 points)**

1. Yo arreglo mi cuarto.	presente
2. Alicia pasó la aspiradora por la sala.	pasado
3. Mis hermanos sacaron toda la basura.	pasado
4. Tú preparas una paella valenciana, ¿verdad?	presente
5. Yo limpio la cocina ahora para ayudar a mi mamá.	presente
6. ¿Trabajó Ud. en Madrid, Sr. Murillo?	pasado

2. **Listen to the following sentences. They will not be repeated. If the second sentence is a logical response to the first, circle the letter *L*. If the sentence is illogical, circle *I*. (6 points)**

1. ¿Tu hermano va a lavar la ropa? Quizás, ya la está lavando.	L
2. Voy a preparar la paella para la fiesta. ¿Te puedo ayudar a preparar la paella?	L
3. Tenemos que colgar la ropa. Sí, la voy a barrer.	I
4. ¿Conchita está pasando la aspiradora? No, no voy a cocinar paella esta noche.	I
5. ¿Cuándo me puedes limpiar las paredes? Ellos están trayéndolas ahora.	I
6. Tenemos una fiesta en nuestra casa mañana. ¿Vamos a adornar la casa?	L

3. **Listen to the following sentences. If the sentence contains a household chore, circle the word *sí*. If it does not, circle the word *no*. (6 points)**

1. Margarita acaba de colgar la ropa.	sí
2. Mi tía va a ayudarme con mi lección de piano.	no
3. ¿Cuándo me puedes limpiar el piso?	sí
4. Me gustaría hacer la tarea en la biblioteca.	no
5. Acabo de ver televisión.	no
6. Ellas acaban de recoger la mesa.	sí

4. **You will hear several sentences about the illustration. Write the letter of the area of the illustration that best corresponds to each sentence you hear. (10 points)**

1. Mario está barriendo el piso.	B
2. Él está trayendo pan y leche.	C
3. Esta noche mamá está preparándonos una paella valenciana.	B
4. Mi hermano está sacando toda la basura.	A

5. El señor acaba de ir de compras. C
6. Primero, termino con las ventanas, y luego voy a hacer las camas. A
7. Ella va a necesitar una olla grande. B
8. Mamá está pasando la aspiradora por la sala. A
9. Adriana está limpiando las ventanas. A
10. Clara está buscando la receta para la paella. B

5. Listen to the following short paragraphs. After each paragraph you will hear two statements about what you heard. Circle the letter *C* if a statement is true, or *F* if it is false. (8 points)

Voy a tener una fiesta y va a venir mucha gente. Tengo que adornar la casa y limpiarla bien. Mi amiga Gloria me va a ayudar. Si ella lava las ventanas, yo puedo pasar la aspiradora, y podemos arreglar la sala juntas.

1. Ella tiene que darle de comer a los gatos, antes de la fiesta. F
2. Su amiga la va a ayudar. C

Estamos en el mes de abril. Cuando llega la primavera a mi mamá le gusta limpiar toda la casa. Hoy tengo que ayudar a mamá a hacer los quehaceres. Primero, tengo que lavarle todas las paredes. Luego, debo barrerle la cocina y pasar la aspiradora por toda la casa.

3. A la mamá le gusta cocinar paella en la primavera. F
4. Hay muchos quehaceres en la primavera. C

Los sábados siempre limpio mi cuarto por la mañana. Hago mi cama, barro y limpio el piso, cuelgo mi ropa y saco la basura. Por la tarde, mi amiga Silvia llega y oímos CDs en mi cuarto limpio.

5. Los sábados por la mañana limpia el cuarto. C
6. Su amiga, Silvia, le ayuda a limpiar el cuarto. F

Me llamo Pablo. Cuando llego de la escuela tengo que hacer los quehaceres de la casa. Primero, tengo que colgar mi ropa. Luego, tengo que sacar la basura y pasar la aspiradora por toda la casa. Cuando termino, hago mi tarea.

7. Cuando llega de la escuela, primero Pablo hace su tarea. F
8. El hermano de Pablo le cuelga la ropa. F

END OF LISTENING COMPREHENSION TEST

Written Test

6. Complete the following sentences, circling the letter of the word that most logically completes each sentence. (4 points)

1. C 2. A 3. A 4. C

7. **Complete the sentences with the appropriate present-tense form of the verb in parentheses to say what each person is doing to prepare for a party at a nearby community shelter. (4 points)**

   1. recoge 2. dirijo 3. prepara 4. colgamos

8. **Complete the following sentences with the correct present-tense form of the verb *traer* to indicate who is bringing what to the party. (5 points)**

   1. traemos 2. traigo 3. traen 4. trae 5. traes

9. **Complete the following sentences with the correct present- tense form of the verb *oír* to indicate what various people hear the day of the party. (5 points)**

   1. oyes 2. oímos 3. oyen 4. oigo 5. oye

10. **Circle the letter of the most appropriate phrase to clarify or to emphasize to whom or for whom the following things are being done. (5 points)**

    1. B 2. C 3. A 4. B 5. B

11. **Rewrite the following sentences, replacing the words in italics with indirect object pronouns. (8 points)**

    1. Ellos me están buscando un libro./...están buscándome un libro. 2. Tomás nos está recogiendo los platos./...está recogiéndonos los platos. 3. Le estoy comprando leche./Estoy comprándole leche. 4. Uds. la están ayudando a preparar la paella./...están ayudándola....

12. **Complete the following paragraph with the preterite tense of the verbs in parentheses. (8 points)**

    1. limpié 2. saqué 3. colgué 4. pasé 5. ayudó 6. trabajamos 7. compraron 8. preparaste

13. **Complete the following paragraph logically using the words shown. Not all answer choices are used. (7 points)**

    1. ayudar 2. quehaceres 3. pone 4. lavar 5. arregla 6. arreglar 7. aspiradora

14. **Tell what the following people have just done by using the expression *acabar de* and the cue suggested by each picture. (5 points)**

    1. acabo de barrer el piso 2. acaba de hacer las camas 3. acaban de poner la mesa 4. acabas de lavar/limpiar las ventanas 5. acabamos de sacar la basura

15. **Write the letter of the word or phrase in the column on the right that connects logically with the information about Spain shown in the column on the left. Some answer choices may not be used. (5 points)**

    1. B 2. G 3. A 4. E 5. C

16. **Write a paragraph consisting of at least four sentences in Spanish describing how you and your family help with the household chores. Be as specific as possible, including who does the chores and when. You may make up any information you wish. (8 points)**

Creative self-expression.

CAPÍTULO 8

Lección 16

Listening Comprehension Test

1. **Listen carefully to the following sentences. They will not be repeated. If the second sentence is a logical response to the first, circle the letter *L*. If it is illogical, circle *I*. (10 points)**

1.	¿Te importa si compramos los guisantes frescos o en latas? No, a mí no me importa.	L
2.	Tú puedes limpiar la cocina tan rápidamente como yo. No, yo puedo limpiarla más rápidamente que tú.	L
3.	¿Te importa si hay más de diez manzanas y menos de diez naranjas? No, no me importa.	L
4.	¿Qué le hace falta para hacer la paella? Me hace falta una cebolla y el arroz.	L
5.	¿Qué te parece, hay tantas fresas aquí como uvas? Me parece que las manzanas están más maduras.	I
6.	¿Qué te parecen mejores, estos tomates o aquellos tomates? Me parece que aquellos tomates están mejores.	L
7.	¿Te importa comprar esos aguacates? Me hacen falta las comidas en lata.	I
8.	No hay tanto pimiento como sal en la receta. No, el mercado no tiene zanahorias.	I
9.	Me parece que a Uds. les hace falta comprar el pollo y el chorizo. Sí, y ahora vamos al mercado a comprarlos.	L
10.	Estas manzanas son más grandes que aquellas manzanas, ¿verdad? No, aquellas manzanas son más grandes y más frescas.	L

2. **You will hear a series of sentences. Listen carefully, they will not be repeated. If a sentence contains a form of the comparative, circle the letter *C;* if a sentence contains a form of the superlative, circle *S.* (10 points)**

1.	Esas cebollas son malas, pero estas cebollas son peores.	C
2.	Don Joaquín es el más interesante de los abuelos en nuestra familia.	S
3.	La paella que hago es la mejor paella de todas.	S
4.	Los tomates de este mercado son más frescos que los tomates de aquel mercado.	C
5.	Los guisantes en lata son más pequeños que los guisantes frescos.	C
6.	El mejor supermercado de nuestra ciudad cierra los domingos.	S
7.	El café que hago en casa es mejor que el café del restaurante.	C
8.	Esta olla es tan pequeña como la otra.	C
9.	Gabriel es el mayor estudiante de la clase.	S
10.	Viviana es menor que Marcela.	C

3. **Listen carefully to the following sentences. If a sentence refers to a past event, circled the word *pasado*; if a sentence mentions something that is occurring in the present, circle the word *presente.* (8 points)**

1. Señor, le di el mejor precio.	pasado
2. Chicos, olvidaron comprar el maíz para las arepas.	pasado
3. Clara añade dos tazas de agua al arroz.	presente
4. Tú llevas helado para el postre.	presente
5. Pedro y Rocío estuvieron en el mercado ayer.	pasado
6. Le damos cuarenta pesetas por ese jamón.	presente
7. Escogiste las mejores verduras.	pasado
8. Estamos comiendo tanto como ayer.	presente

4. **You will hear several sentences about food and food preparation. Write the letter of the illustration that best corresponds with each sentence you hear. (10 points)**

1. Me parece que esa lechuga es mejor que esta lechuga.	A
2. Por la mañana voy a preparar huevos con jamón.	B
3. Quiero hacer una ensalada y me hacen falta la lechuga, los tomates y las zanahorias.	A
4. Me hacen falta los guisantes para hacer una paella.	A
5. Los ingredientes que necesito son el queso, la leche y un poco de jamón.	B
6. Me gustaría saber si esas papas son mejores que las otras.	A
7. No puedo hacer esta receta sin huevos, leche y queso.	B
8. El viernes voy a cocinar el pescado con arroz.	B
9. No me gustan aquellas fresas; prefiero esas fresas.	A
10. Aquellos plátanos no están tan maduros como esos plátanos.	A

END OF LISTENING COMPREHENSION TEST

Written Test

5. **Circle the letter of the word in each group that most logically does not belong. (6 points)**

   1. A 2. A 3. B 4. B 5. C 6. C

6. **Tell what happened yesterday, using the preterite tense of each verb indicated in parentheses. (12 points)**

   1. di 2. recordaste 3. llegamos 4. dejaste 5. preparó 6. empecé 7. gustó
   8. arreglaron 9. apagué 10. dimos 11. acabamos 12. dimos

7. **Complete the following sentences with the preterite tense of the verb *estar* to ask or say where these people were yesterday at 6:00 P.M. (5 points)**

   1. estuvimos 2. estuve 3. estuvieron 4. estuvo 5. estuviste

8. Compare the indicated items, according to the information provided for each of two markets. (10 points)

Possible answers:
1. El primer mercado tiene más ajo que el segundo mercado. 2. Los plátanos del primer mercado son mejores que los plátanos del segundo mercado. 3. Los tomates del primer mercado son más grandes que los tomates del segundo mercado. 4. Los guisantes del primer mercado son más frescos que los guisantes del segundo mercado. 5. El primer mercado tiene menos pescado que el segundo mercado.

9. Write five logical statements in Spanish about people and objects in your life, using the appropriate form of the superlative and the provided cues. Be sure to mention the group to which the person or object is being compared, (in the class, in my house and so forth). You may make up any information you wish. (10 points)

Possible answers:
1. La persona más joven de mi familia es *(name of person).* 2. La fruta más dulce de todas las frutas es (*name of fruit*). 3. El restaurante *(name of restaurant)* es el mejor restaurante de la ciudad. 4. El programa *(name of television program)* es el peor programa de la televisión. 5. La comida más popular del colegio es (*name of food*).

10. In Spanish, list three images that are commonly associated with Spain. Then explain your answer in English (or in Spanish if you can). (3 points)

Possible answers:
1. la paella: *It is an internationally known food that originated in Spain.* 2. los romanos: *They brought Latin to Spain, which evolved into Spanish.* 3. las playas bonitas: *Spain has many beautiful beaches along its extensive coastline.*

11. Read the following paragraph. Then answer the questions in Spanish in complete sentences. (8 points)

Possible answers:
1. Preparó la comida el sábado pasado. 2. Preparó una sopa de pollo y una paella. 3. Compró unas cebollas, los guisantes y el ajo. 4. Su hermano sacó la basura y su mamá la ayudó a lavar los platos.

12. Write a paragraph of at least four complete sentences in Spanish in which you tell about your last trip to the supermarket. Name the store and state when you were there. Then mention two or three of the items you purchased. Conclude by stating whether you liked or did not enjoy shopping for food at that supermarket, and when you will be going to the supermarket again. You may make up any of the information you wish. (8 points)

Creative self-expression.

CAPÍTULO 9

Lección 17

Listening Comprehension Test

1. **Listen to the following sentences. They will not be repeated. If the second sentence is a logical response to the first, circle the letter *L*. If it is illogical, circle *I*.** (10 points)

1.	No voy a comprar aquellos zapatos. Yo tampoco quiero comprarlos. Son muy caros.	L
2.	¿Qué compraste ayer? No compré nada. No vi ningún vestido que me gustó.	L
3.	¿Quién te ayudó a escoger este vestido anaranjado? Nadie me ayudó. Yo fui sola a la tienda.	L
4.	No me gustan los sombreros. A mí me gustan también.	I
5.	Quiero comprar un nuevo traje de baño porque el que tengo no me queda bien. Muy bien señorita. ¿De qué color lo prefiere?	L
6.	¿Prefieres el suéter rosado o el azul? Prefiero el azul.	L
7.	¿Qué día fuiste al centro comercial? Durmieron hasta las dos.	I
8.	¿Quién fue al estadio con Isabel y Cristina el sábado pasado? Daniel y Tito fueron buenos deportistas.	I
9.	¿Dónde consiguieron los zapatos de tacón? Esta chaqueta no me queda bien.	I
10.	¿Es de algodón o de seda tu camisa? Mi hermano compró dos camisas de seda.	I

2. **You will hear several sentences. They will be repeated. If the sentence you hear includes an article of clothing, circle the word *sí*. If it does not, circle the word *no*.** (9 points)

1.	Como te prometí, en junio vamos de vacaciones a Panamá.	no
2.	Te cuento que el rosado no te queda bien.	no
3.	Decidí comprar el traje de baño.	sí
4.	Cuando fui al centro comercial no compré nada.	no
5.	¿Cuándo compraste los guantes?	sí
6.	¿Cuántas camisas compraste?	sí
7.	Está lloviendo pero no me importa porque tengo mi impermeable.	sí
8.	Estas servilletas son de algodón.	no
9.	Estos calcetines no me quedan bien.	sí

3. **Listen carefully to several statements in Spanish. Circle the word *pretérito* if what you hear refers to something in the past. Circle the word *presente* if the statement refers to something in the present.** (8 points)

1.	¿Quién durmió mal ayer?	pretérito
2.	¿Leíste el periódico ayer?	pretérito
3.	Nunca le prometo nada a nadie.	presente

4.	Nosotros fuimos gordos, ahora no.	pretérito
5.	¿Te repitió el número de teléfono?	pretérito
6.	Estos pantalones le quedan bien.	presente
7.	¡Oye! ¿Ves la mano de Gloria y el anillo nuevo que tiene en el dedo?	presente
8.	No voy nunca sin mi impermeable.	presente

4. You will hear several questions in Spanish. Circle the letter of the logical response to each. (6 points)

1.	Perdón señor, ¿le gusta alguna camisa?	C
2.	¿Qué vas a comprar, la blusa de seda o el vestido de algodón?	B
3.	¿Buscaste algunos calcetines?	B
4.	¿Quieres comprar algo?	A
5.	¿Vienen Dolores y Lucía mañana?	B
6.	Buenos días señora. ¿Le puedo ayudar con algo?	B

5. Listen carefully to several short paragraphs in Spanish. They will be repeated. After each you will hear two statements about what you heard. Circle the letter *C* if a statement is true, or *F* if it is false. (8 points)

Teresa va de vacaciones en diciembre a visitar a sus primos que viven en Chicago. Hace mucho frío allá, y ella tiene que comprar ropa para el viaje. Ayer compró un abrigo, guantes y botas. Todavía le hacen falta unos pantalones y unos suéteres de lana.

1.	Sus primos viven en Miami.	F
2.	Teresa va de vacaciones en el invierno.	C

Trabajo en una tienda de ropa de hombres. Todo el día vendo ropa. Ayer vendí dos trajes de baño, cinco suéteres, dieciséis camisas y doce corbatas. Muchas personas me pidieron ayuda. Me gusta mi trabajo en la tienda de ropa.

3.	Él trabaja en una tienda de ropa de mujeres.	F
4.	Muchas personas le pidieron ayuda.	C

Esteban y Víctor fueron de compras ayer. Fueron al centro comercial y entraron en muchas tiendas de ropa. Esteban compró un traje de lana gris y Víctor compró dos corbatas y una camisa blanca.

5.	Los dos muchachos compraron ropa de hombre.	C
6.	No encontraron ningún traje de lana.	F

Ayer fui a las tiendas para buscar unos zapatos nuevos. Vi zapatos bajos y zapatos de tacones de todos los colores. Vi unos zapatos rojos pero no me gustaron porque nunca llevo nada rojo. También vi zapatos de color café, pero tampoco tengo ninguna ropa de ese color. Decidí comprar unos zapatos negros bajos porque puedo combinarlos con toda mi ropa.

7.	La muchacha fue a las tiendas para buscar unos zapatos nuevos.	C
8.	Decidió comprar unas botas de tacones.	F

END OF LISTENING COMPREHENSION TEST

Written Test

6. **Complete the following dialog logically, choosing from the words and expressions in the box. Not all answer choices are used. (8 points)**

   1. también 2. alguien 3. nadie 4. algo 5. tampoco 6. nunca 7. nada 8. ni

7. **Complete these sentences with the appropriate preterite-tense form of the verbs in parentheses. (8 points)**

   1. pidió 2. vendiste 3. escribieron 4. escribió 5. preferimos 6. prefirió
   7. durmieron 8. dormí

8. **Complete these statements logically, circling the letter of the correct response for each. (5 points)**

   1. A 2. C 3. C 4. B 5. A

9. **Complete the paragraph with the appropriate preterite-tense form of the verbs in parentheses. (8 points)**

   1. fui 2. compramos 3. consiguió 4. fuimos 5. pedimos 6. Comimos
   7. decidieron 8. Fue

10. **Read the following statements about *Panamá.* Write the letter *C* if a statement is true or *F* if it is false. (6 points)**

    1. F 2. F 3. C 4. C 5. C 6. C

11. **Read the following paragraph. Then answer the questions that follow in complete sentences in Spanish. (10 points)**

    Possible Answers:
    1. Fueron a comprar ropa para el invierno. 2. Primero Beatriz escogió unos suéteres de lana. 3. Ana María no compró ningún suéter. 4. No compró nada. 5. Necesitan comprar unas faldas.

12. **Answer the following questions negatively in complete sentences. Follow the model. (6 points)**

    Possible answers:
    1. No, no veo a nadie en esa tienda. 2. No, no tengo ningún anillo nuevo.
    3. No voy a comprar ni el suéter ni el impermeable.

13. **Imagine that you and one of your friends went shopping yesterday in the store pictured below. Using the preterite tense, write a paragraph of at least four complete sentences in Spanish in which you describe your shopping trip. Be sure to tell what you bought and what your friend chose. You may make up any information you wish about colors, fabrics, fit and prices. (8 points)**

    Creative self-expression.

CAPÍTULO 9

Lección 18

Listening Comprehension Test

1. **Listen to the following statements and questions that you might hear in a department store. When they are repeated, write the missing words in the spaces provided. (5 points)**

   1. Esta falda es demasiado larga.
   2. ¿Tienes bastante dinero, mamá?
   3. ¿Qué material prefiere Ud., señora?
   4. Estos pañuelos son de buena calidad.
   5. Perdón, ¿qué tamaño usa Ud.?

2. **Listen to the following sentences. They will not be repeated. If the second sentence is a logical response to the first, circle the letter *L.* If it is illogical, circle *I.* (8 points)**

   1. ¿Quién te dijo que mañana los pantalones están en oferta? — L
      Nadie me lo dijo. Lo leí en el periódico.
   2. ¿Cuándo fue la última vez que tuviste que ir al departamento de regalos? — I
      Fui al banco ayer.
   3. ¿Cuándo oíste que Patricia tuvo que ir a Ecuador? — I
      Sí, Marta tuvo que estudiar.
   4. ¿Te parece que Vanesa dijo la verdad? — L
      Me parece que sí. Ella nunca dice mentiras.
   5. ¿Leíste el periódico hoy? — L
      Si, ya lo leí.
   6. ¿Le dijiste a Camilo que vamos a ir en mi carro? — L
      Sí, ya se lo dije.
   7. ¿Qué te dijo Mateo cuando oyó las noticias de su amiga? — L
      No me dijo nada, pero la llamó.
   8. ¿Dijeron por qué? — I
      Sí, Antonio va a volver.

3. **Listen carefully to several questions and statements in Spanish. Circle the word *pretérito* if what you hear refers to something in the past. Circle the word *presente* if the statement refers to something in the present. (8 points)**

   1. Están haciendo compras. — presente
   2. Tuvo que salir. — pretérito
   3. Les dije que todo está en oferta. — pretérito
   4. Te vi anteayer en el centro comercial. — pretérito
   5. Veo a mis amigos todos los días. — presente
   6. ¿Qué leíste en esa revista? — pretérito
   7. ¿Oyeron Uds. la radio esta mañana? — pretérito
   8. ¿Qué hiciste hoy? — pretérito

4. **You will hear several sentences about some of the items shown. Listen carefully, the sentences will not be repeated. Write the letter of the illustration that best corresponds with each sentence you hear. (10 points)**

1. Pienso comprar este pijama, me gusta la calidad. C
2. Mi tío que vive en Quito siempre lleva botas de cuero como aquellas. B
3. Nicolás dijo que Manuel quiere una billetera de cuero para su cumpleaños. C
4. Sonia dice que le gustaría tener ese perfume para su cumpleaños. ¿Qué te parece el precio? ¿Es demasiado caro o no? A
5. Mi tío siempre quiere pañuelos y corbatas para su cumpleaños. C
6. No sé cual me gusta más, este collar de perlas o ese collar de oro. A
7. Blanca no tiene una bufanda para el invierno pero quiere una roja. A
8. ¡Qué lindo son esos aretes de plata! A
9. Graciela dijo que Lucía quiere un bolso de cuero como este bolso. B
10. Este cinturón de cuero es perfecto para mi primo, Ángel. B

5. **Listen carefully to several short paragraphs. After each you will hear two statements about what you heard. Circle the letter *C* if a statement is true, or *F* if it is false. (6 points)**

Quiero comprar un bolso pero no sé si lo quiero de material sintético o de cuero. Tampoco no sé si lo quiero negro o café. Leí en el periódico que hay algunos en oferta hoy. Voy a llamar a Adriana para ver si ella quiere ir de compras conmigo al centro comercial.

1. Ella va a comprar un bolso de cuero blanco. F
2. Ella leyó en el periódico que hay bolsos en oferta hoy. C

A mis padres no les gustan las tarjetas de crédito, y las usan poco. Ellos piensan que es mejor pagar en efectivo que a crédito. Me parece que eso es verdad, pero las tarjetas de crédito son muy importantes en nuestro país.

3. Los padres dicen que las tarjetas de crédito son importantes, y las usan mucho. F
4. Los padres piensan que es mejor pagar en efectivo. C

Ayer fui al cine. Carlos y Juan fueron conmigo. Después del cine fuimos a comer a un restaurante al lado del cine. Comimos una pizza. Antes de ir a casa fuimos a jugar a las maquinitas. ¡Fue una noche muy divertida!

5. Los muchachos fueron al cine, a comer y a jugar a las maquinitas. C
6. Fueron a casa antes de jugar a las maquinitas. F

6. **You will hear a paragraph in Spanish, followed by several questions. Listen carefully, the information will not be repeated. Answer the questions you hear by circling the letter of the most appropriate response to each. (5 points)**

   Es el Día de las Madres y Esteban y Carlos van de compras para buscar regalos para sus madres. Esteban quiere comprar unos aretes y un bolso para su madre y Carlos quiere comprar un collar y un perfume para su madre. Van al centro comercial porque Esteban dice que allí tienen de todo. Los dos saben que esas cosas cuestan mucho y por eso llevan bastante dinero en efectivo para pagar todo.

   1. ¿Por qué van al centro comercial Esteban y Carlos? A
   2. ¿Qué quiere comprarle Esteban para su madre? A
   3. ¿Qué busca Carlos para su madre? B
   4. ¿Qué saben los dos? C
   5. ¿Cómo van a pagar? B

END OF LISTENING COMPREHENSION TEST

Written Test

7. **Complete the statements, circling the letter of the most logical choice for each statement. (8 points)**

   1. B 2. A 3. C 4. B 5. A 6. C 7. B 8. A

8. **Complete the following sentences logically with an appropriate word or expression from the list that follows. Not all answers choices are used. (6 points)**

   1. sin ti 2. al lado de nosotros 3. para ella 4. lejos de él 5. conmigo 6. antes que ellos

9. **Complete these sentences with the appropriate preterite-tense form of the verbs in parentheses. (10 points)**

   1. dije 2. oyó 3. hicieron 4. vieron 5. tuve 6. vio 7. Recibiste 8. dieron 9. leyó 10. Pagaron

10. **Complete the following paragraph, choosing your answers from among the words in the box. Not all answer choices are used. (10 points)**

    1. algodón 2. tienda 3. periódico 4. camisas 5. buena 6. ahorrar 7. escalera 8. ascensor 9. contigo 10. precios

11. **Write the letter of the word or name in the column on the right that best answers the questions in the column on the left. Not all answer choices are used. (6 points)**

    1. A 2. G 3. C 4. D 5. H 6. F

12. **Read the following paragraph. Then answer the questions that follow in complete sentences in Spanish. (10 points)**

Possible answers:
1. Fueron a comprar regalos para la amiga de Esperanza y la hermanita de Víctor.
2. Dijo que le gustaría un collar y una pulsera. 3. La fiesta de Mercedes es esta noche.
4. Los aretes son de plata. 5. Después de comprar todo fueron a tomar un refresco y hablaron de lo que acabaron de comprar.

13. **Write at least four sentences about going shopping last Christmas. Include where you went, how you went there, with whom you went, what you bought and for whom, what you saw and any other information you would like. You may make up any of the information you wish. (8 points)**

Creative self-expression.

CAPÍTULO 10

Lección 19

Listening Comprehension Test

1. **Listen to the following sentences about what some people did this past weekend. Circle the word *sí* if what you hear refers to a leisure activity. Circle the word *no*, if it does not. (8 points)**

1. Jorge estudió para un examen.	no
2. Yo fui de compras con mis hermanas.	sí
3. Esteban y Margarita limpiaron las ventanas.	no
4. Mis padres comieron en un restaurante del centro.	sí
5. Tú jugaste al béisbol con tus hermanos.	sí
6. Andrés y yo barrimos la cocina.	no
7. Uds. montaron en bicicleta.	sí
8. Anita y Susana arreglaron la casa.	no

2. **Listen to the following questions heard during a poll. If the question comes from a poll about classes, circle the word *clase*. If it is about stores and their merchandise, circle the word *tienda*. (8 points)**

1. ¿Por qué prefiere Ud. venir de compras aquí?	tienda
2. ¿Cuál es la clase más interesante de tu horario?	clase
3. ¿Le gustan más estas blusas de seda o aquellas de algodón?	tienda
4. ¿Por qué piensa Ud. que ella es la mejor profesora?	clase
5. ¿Piensa Ud. que los precios son mejores aquí que en otras tiendas?	tienda
6. ¿Cuál es su clase favorita?	clase
7. Cuando va de compras, ¿prefiere pagar a crédito o en efectivo?	tienda
8. ¿Cuántos estudiantes hay en su clase de español?	clase

3. **You will hear several sentences. Listen carefully, they will not be repeated. Based upon what you hear, circle the letter of the response that indicates what these people have to do. (6 points)**

1. Tú vas a ir a la playa, pero no tienes nada para llevar. A
2. Ana y Javier preparan una paella, pero les hacen falta unos ingredientes. C
3. Patricia tiene un examen de matemáticas mañana, pero no comprende mucho. A
4. Yo voy a dar una fiesta, pero mi casa está muy sucia. B
5. Fernando no tiene nada para el cumpleaños de su mamá. C
6. Uds. quieren jugar fútbol en el equipo de su colegio. B

4. **You will hear several sentences in Spanish. Write the letter of the illustration that best corresponds to each sentence you hear. (10 points)**

1. Esta clase es interesante, pero a veces es muy aburrida también. B
2. Les gusta mucho caminar. A
3. ¿Cuándo visitaron Marcos y Elena las ruinas incas? A
4. ¿Cuál prefieres, esta blusa de seda o esta de algodón? C
5. Las matemáticas es mi clase menos favorita. B
6. ¿Vas a pagarla en efectivo o con tarjeta de crédito? C
7. Me gustaría mucho viajar al Perú. A
8. A los estudiantes les importan mucho las matemáticas. B
9. Voy a hacerle una pregunta a la mujer que está cerca de la caja. C
10. ¿Están esos vestidos en oferta especial? C

5. **Listen carefully to several short paragraphs. After each you will hear two statements about what you heard. Circle the letter *C* if a statement is true, or *F* if it is false. (10 points)**

Me llamo Paz. El fin de semana pasado tuve que trabajar en un proyecto para la clase de español. Fui a la biblioteca y leí mucho sobre los incas. No tuve tiempo para salir con mis amigos o limpiar mi cuarto.

1. Paz tuvo que limpiar su cuarto el fin de semana pasado. F
2. Paz trabajó en un proyecto para la clase de inglés. F

Me llamo Miguel. En dos semanas mi familia y yo vamos de vacaciones a México. Yo pienso nadar y caminar por la playa, y mis padres piensan visitar las pirámides mayas para tomar fotos. Mi hermano Arturo sólo quiere dormir mucho.

3. Los padres de Miguel quieren tomar fotos. C
4. Miguel sólo quiere dormir durante las vacaciones. F

¡Hola! Me llamo Germán. Mañana vamos a dar una fiesta en nuestra casa, y hay mucho que hacer. Mamá tiene que preparar la comida. Papá tiene que comprar los refrescos. Y mis hermanos y yo tenemos que limpiar toda la casa y barrer el garaje. ¡Caramba!

5. Los padres de Germán van a ayudar con la fiesta. C
6. La casa ya está limpia para la fiesta. F

Ayer fui de compras con mi mamá porque vamos de vacaciones a Bariloche este invierno. Compré un suéter de lana y una bufanda de algodón. Mi mamá compró botas negras, pero a mí no me gustaron. Necesito volver a la tienda para buscar un pantalón de lana.

7. Ella compró un pantalón de lana. F
8. A ella no le gustaron las botas de su mamá. C

El Perú es un país grande e interesante. Está en la América del Sur. Su capital se llama Lima, y es una ciudad grande y moderna. Muchas personas viven en Lima.

9. El Perú está en la América Central. F
10. Lima es la capital del Perú. C

END OF LISTENING COMPREHENSION TEST

Written Test

6. Complete the following sentences with the appropriate preterite-tense form of the verbs in parentheses to tell what everyone did last weekend. (10 points)

1. fueron 2. vio 3. di 4. tomé 5. estuviste 6. hicimos 7. durmieron 8. comimos 9. estuvo 10. leyó

7. Rearrange the following sentences in a logical order to explain what Pilar did on Saturday afternoon. The first one has been done for you. (10 points)

1. (A) 2. F 3. C 4. D 5. J 6. K 7. G 8. H 9. I 10. E 11. B

8. Read the following paragraph. Then answer the questions that follow in complete sentences in Spanish. (10 points)

1. Tiene dieciséis años. 2. La clase es muy difícil. 3. Ella es amable. 4. Juega al tenis con su mejor amigo. 5. Fernando y su mejor amigo, Alfredo, son los mejores.

9. Read the following information about Peru and the Inca civilization. Write the letter *C* if a statement is true or *F* if it is false. (10 points)

1. C 2. F 3. F 4. C 5. C 6. F 7. C 8. C 9. F 10. F

10. Answer the following questions in Spanish, using complete sentences. (8 points)

Answers will vary.

11. Look at the following illustrations showing what Javier did last weekend. Write a paragraph of at least five complete sentences in Spanish in which you describe some of the activities he did and where he did these activities. Add as many details as possible. (10 points)

Creative self-expression.

CAPÍTULO 10

Lección 20

Listening Comprehension Test

1. Listen to the following statements. When each is repeated, write the missing words in the spaces provided. (5 points)

1. Algún día, me gustaría ir a Guatemala.
2. A mí me gustaría ir a unas ruinas mayas.
3. En el verano me gustaría trabajar en un hotel.
4. Mi amigo ideal es inteligente y generoso.
5. Mi amiga ideal es dulce y divertida.

2. Listen carefully to the following sentences and questions. If the sentence or question you hear contains a summer job, circle the word *sí*. If it does not, circle the word *no*. (8 points)

1. A Arturo le gusta jugar al tenis con su mejor amigo. — no
2. Ana trabaja en un supermercado. — sí
3. Inés vende ropa en una tienda de deportes. — sí
4. David siempre va de compras a las tiendas del centro comercial. — no
5. Beto es mesero en el Café Royal, ¿verdad? — sí
6. Guillermo prepara comida en un restaurante mexicano. — sí
7. Ernesto y yo bailamos merengue todos los fines de semana. — no
8. Tomás, tú trabajas en un banco, ¿no? — sí

3. Listen carefully to the following pairs of sentences. They will not be repeated. If the second sentence is a logical response to the first, circle the letter *L*. If it is illogical, circle the letter *I*. (7 points)

1. Acabo de recibir una carta por correo electrónico de un muchacho en Cancún. — L
   ¡Qué interesante! ¿Qué dijo él?
2. Me gustaría viajar a Guatemala y a México. — I
   No, Cuernavaca no es la capital de México.
3. Los Sánchez piensan ir de vacaciones a Miami en dos semanas. — L
   Y ¿qué van a hacer en una ciudad tan grande?
4. Necesito hablar español para poder trabajar en un hotel en México. — I
   Sí, hay buenos hoteles en Guatemala.
5. Natalia es una muchacha muy guapa, ¿no? — I
   Sí, y hace frío también.
6. ¿Es cómico tu mejor amigo? — L
   Sí, a mí me gustan las personas divertidas.
7. ¿Cuál es tu pasatiempo favorito? — I
   Siempre voy en metro.

4. **You will hear several sentences that describe the people in this illustration. They will not be repeated. Circle the name of the person that each sentence describes. (10 points)**

1. Es el muchacho más alto de todos.	Germán
2. Ella es la chica más delgada de nuestra clase y es muy amable.	María
3. Él es calvo, es nuestro profesor de matemáticas.	Roberto
4. Ella es morena y muy guapa.	Isabel
5. Ella es baja y le gusta jugar al béisbol.	María
6. Es gordo, muy simpático e inteligente.	Roberto
7. Ella es muy rápida y le gusta el tenis.	Isabel
8. Le gusta mucho el básquetbol.	Germán
9. Le gusta leer muchos libros, no es tonto.	Roberto
10. Su ropa está sucia.	María

5. **Listen carefully to the following questions. Then circle the letter of the most logical response for each. (8 points)**

1. ¿Cómo es tu amigo ideal?	B
2. ¿Adónde te gustaría ir de vacaciones?	B
3. ¿Trabajó Bárbara en el supermercado el verano pasado?	A
4. ¿Qué hiciste el fin de semana pasado?	A
5. ¿Cuál es el pasatiempo favorito de tu amigo por correo electrónico?	A
6. ¿Cuántos años tiene tu amigo?	A
7. ¿Cuál es su dirección?	B
8. ¿Qué te gustaría ser?	B

END OF LISTENING COMPREHENSION TEST

Written Test

6. **Match the jobs in the column on the left with the most appropriate description in the column on the right. Write the letter in the space provided. (8 points)**

   1. C 2. F 3. D 4. G 5. B 6. A 7. E 8. H

7. **Complete the following description of Hilda's weekend. Write the appropriate forms of the verbs in parentheses in the space provided. You must decide whether the verb is in the preterite, the present or the present progressive. (12 points)**

   1. fue 2. estuve 3. tuve 4. ayudó 5. pienso 6. puedo 7. viendo 8. vamos
   9. fue 10. quiere 11. pensando 12. sé

8. **Complete this dialogue between Marisol and Esteban, using the words from the box. Not all answer choices are used. (10 points)**

   1. estuviste 2. fui 3. enfermo 4. que 5. hacer 6. ir 7. nadar 8. comer
   9. contigo 10. Nadie

9. **Read the following statements about Guatemala and the Mayan civilization. Write the letter *C* if the statement is true or *F* if it is false. (10 points)**

   1. F 2. F 3. F 4. C 5. F 6. C 7. C 8. C 9. F 10. F

10. **Imagine that you have a key pal from Guatemala. In her latest e-mail she asks you the following questions about yourself. Answer them in Spanish in complete sentences. (12 points)**

Possible answers:
1. Soy de (los) Estados Unidos. 2. Vivo con mis padres y mis hermanos. 3. Estudio español, inglés e historia. 4. Juego al béisbol. 5. Soy alto, rubio, inteligente y muy simpático. 6. Yo fui al cine, trabajé en el supermercado y dormí mucho.

11. **Write a paragraph in which you describe your best friend with at least five complete sentences in Spanish. Include the following information in your composition. (10 points)**

Creative self-expression.

ACHIEVEMENT TEST II

Listening Comprehension Test

1. **Listen to the following sentences. They will not be repeated. If the second sentence is a logical response to the first, circle the letter *L*. If it is illogical, circle the letter *I*. (10 points)**

1.	¿Piensas que aquellos tomates están frescos? A Héctor no le gusta preparar la comida.	I
2.	Tenemos que ir al segundo piso. ¿Por qué no tomamos la escalera automática?	L
3.	¿Qué está haciendo Gloria? Es muy lindo, ¿verdad?	I
4.	Pedro, ¿estás durmiendo o viendo televisión? Yo tengo la lista de programas.	I
5.	¿Juegas a las cartas? No, juego a las damas.	L
6.	¿Cuánto tiempo hace que no juegas al fútbol? Hace un mes, más o menos.	L
7.	¿Cuándo ves la televisión? La veo por la noche.	L
8.	¿A qué hora vuelves del cine? Prefiero ir a la fiesta.	I
9.	¿Cuánto tiempo hace que tienes ese pasatiempo? Hace cuatro años.	L
10.	¿Dónde pagamos? En la caja.	L

2. **You will hear several sentences in Spanish. They will not be repeated, so listen carefully. If a sentence refers to clothing, circle the word *ropa*. If the sentence refers to food, circle the word *comida*. (8 points)**

1.	Fueron a comprar pollo.	comida
2.	¿No le gustó aquella blusa de seda?	ropa
3.	Una libra de carne y dos latas de guisantes, por favor.	comida

4. Claudia me dijo que a Teresa le gustaría una blusa negra. — ropa
5. Me gustaría ir contigo porque necesito unos suéteres y están en oferta hoy. — ropa
6. Esta cebolla parece mejor que esa cebolla allí. — comida
7. ¿Por qué no miramos las botas nuevas en el segundo piso? — ropa
8. ¿Es el arroz el ingrediente más importante de la paella? — comida

3. Listen carefully to the following sentences. If a sentence refers to a past event, circle the word *pasado;* if a sentence mentions something that is occurring right now, circle the word *presente;* if a sentence names an activity that is going to occur later, circle the word *futuro.* (10 points)

1. ¿Por qué no fuiste conmigo? — pasado
2. El viernes pasado jugamos fútbol una hora y después, nadamos veinte minutos. — pasado
3. Ayer estuve en la playa con mis amigos todo el día. — pasado
4. La vi en la tienda. — pasado
5. ¿Qué estás haciendo? — presente
6. La playa es muy divertida cuando está soleada. — presente
7. Traigo unos refrescos fríos conmigo. — presente
8. Gracias, eres muy simpático. ¿Cuándo vas otra vez? — presente
9 No voy a ir porque no tengo transporte. — futuro
10. ¿Van a ir en metro o en autobús? — futuro

4. You will hear several statements about different people. Circle the letter of the most appropriate conclusion to each statement you hear. (5 points)

1. Clara necesita comer algo. — A
2. Paquito tiene tres años y está muy cansado. — B
3. Tú tienes un examen muy importante mañana. — A
4. María y yo vamos a tomar un refresco. — C
5. Arturo está caminando muy rápido. — A

5. You will now hear several sentences about some of the items in this illustration. Write the letter of the illustration that best corresponds to each sentence you hear. (10 points)

1. Voy de compras porque quiero buscar una falda azul con una blusa blanca de seda. — B
2. Después de pasar la aspiradora, voy a barrer el garaje. — C
3. Di de comer al gato y ahora está durmiendo. — C
4. Con este traje necesito unos calcetines negros. — B
5. Me gusta más el invierno cuando puedo esquiar todo el fin de semana. — A
6. Este traje de lana es muy bueno, y me gusta el sombrero también. — B
7. Voy a llevar esos zapatos de tacón con esa falda. — B
8. Si no nieva demasiado, voy a patinar con mis amigos esta tarde. — A
9. Mi padre saca la basura y, después, va al supermercado. — C
10. Cuando hace frío me gusta hacer deportes de invierno. — A

6. You will hear a series of sentences. Listen carefully, they will not be repeated. If a sentence contains a form of the superlative, circle the letter *S;* if a sentence contains a form of the comparative, circle *C.* (7 points)

1. Yo puedo nadar más rápidamente que Isabel. C
2. Felipe es más alto que Viviana. C
3. Sandra es la mayor de los tres hermanos. S
4. Esta papa es mejor que aquella papa. C
5. Estos aguacates no están tan maduros como aquellos aguacates. C
6. No hay tanto pollo como jamón en esa paella. C

7. Listen carefully as several people tell about their lives. After each monolog, you will hear two statements about what you heard. Circle the letter *C* if a statement is true or *F* if it is false. (6 points)

Patinar sobre hielo es muy divertido. En el invierno me gusta ir a patinar. Pero si nieva demasiado, no puedo ir. Voy con mi familia o con mis amigos dos veces a la semana.

1. Si nieva mucho no puede ir a patinar. C
2. Va a patinar con un amigo todos los días de la semana. F

Vivo en Chile. Las estaciones del año aquí son muy diferentes a las estaciones en los Estados Unidos. Por ejemplo, cuando es invierno en Chile, es verano en los Estados Unidos. Cuando es primavera aquí, es otoño allá.

3. En Chile las estaciones del año son diferentes a las estaciones en los Estados Unidos. C
4. Cuando es primavera en Chile es otoño en los Estados Unidos. C

Mi estación favorita es la primavera. Me gusta porque hay muchas flores, hace fresco y puedo hacer muchos deportes.

5. La primavera es muy aburrida. F
6. En la primavera hay muchas flores. C

8. You will hear three people describe how they are feeling and why, followed by several questions. Listen carefully, the information will not be repeated. Circle the letter of the most appropriate response to each question you hear. (9 points)

Me llamo Alberto Rojas. Estoy feliz. Soy patinador sobre ruedas y siempre soy el mejor patinador en las competencias regionales. Son las seis de la mañana y estoy patinando cerca de mi casa. Patino por una hora, cinco días a la semana. El sábado no patino porque monto en mi bicicleta con mis amigos. El domingo estoy con mi familia todo el día.

1. ¿Es Alberto un buen patinador? A
2. ¿Patina él todos los días? B
3. ¿Qué hace los domingos? B

Estoy cansada porque acabo de hacer aeróbicos. Los hice por más de una hora. Ahora tengo mucha sed y voy a tomar un refresco muy frío.

4. ¿Cómo está la chica? A
5. ¿Qué acaba de hacer? C
6. ¿Por cuánto tiempo los hizo? B

Estoy aburrido. Hace mucho frío y no puedo salir a jugar. Voy a llamar a mis amigos para ver si ellos quieren jugar al ajedrez o ver una película conmigo.

7. ¿Por qué no puede salir a jugar? C
8. ¿A quién va a llamar? B
9. ¿Por qué va a llamarlos? C

END OF LISTENING COMPREHENSION TEST

Written Test

9. Circle the word or expression that most logically does not belong in each of the following groups of three. (10 points)

1. B 2. C 3. A 4. C 5. B 6. B 7. C 8. B 9. A 10. C

10. Find the antonyms (words with an opposite meaning) for the italicized words in the column on the right. Then write the letter of that word in the space provided. (10 points)

1. I 2 B 3. G 4. A 5. H 6. C 7. D 8. J 9. E 10. F

11. In Spanish, identify each of the items shown in this illustration. Be sure to include the appropriate definite article for each. (10 points)

1. la corbata 2. la camisa 3. el collar 4. la billetera 5. el vestido 6. los zapatos 7. los guantes 8. los calcetines 9. la falda 10. los aretes

12. Complete the following statements by circling the letter of the most logical conclusion for each. (10 points)

1. A 2. A 3. A 4. B 5. C 6. A 7. B 8. C 9. B 10. A

13. Complete the sentences in Spanish by writing the present-tense of the verb in parentheses. (5 points)

1. copia 2. esquío 3. envío 4. enviamos 5. continúan

14. Complete the following sentences with the appropriate present-tense form of the verbs indicated in parentheses. (14 points)

1. damos 2. pongo 3. piensan 4. juegan 5. Podemos 6. puedo 7. llega 8. dices 9. digo 10. piden 11. tienen 12. queremos 13. oyen 14. salgo

15. Imagine you are in the park surrounded by many different people who are involved in numerous different activities. Using the present progressive, summarizing what various people are doing right now, according to the cues. (5 points)

1. Tú estás corriendo. 2. Unas muchachas están jugando al volibol. 3. Yo estoy hablando español. 4. Tú y yo estamos leyendo. 5. Una mujer está durmiendo.

16. Write the correct preterite-tense form of the indicated verbs to form a logical statement about what the following people did yesterday. (15 points)

1. fue 2. estuvieron 3. hablaron 4. vi 5. tuve 6. salí 7. llegué 8. empecé 9. comimos 10. estuvimos 11. oyeron 12. hizo 13. jugaron 14. leyó 15. hiciste

17. Imagine that you are in the clothing store shown below. Complete the following statements and questions with the appropriate form of the demonstrative adjectives *este, ese* and *aquel.* Follow the model. (6 points)

1. Estos 2. aquel 3. esas 4. estas 5. Aquella 6. esos

18. Complete the following sentences logically, choosing from the words shown in the box. Each answer choices is used once only. (6 points)

1. nunca 2. también 3. nada 4. algo 5. siempre 6. tampoco

19. Look at the illustration of some people in line at the movie ticket booth. Complete the following sentences with an ordinal number to tell who is in which position in line. (5 points)

1. quinto 2. segunda 3. primero 4. sexto 5. séptima

20. Read the following statements about some of the Spanish-speaking countries of the world. Write the letter *C* if a statement is true or *F* if it is false. (9 points)

1. C 2. C 3. C 4. C 5. F 6. C 7. C 8. F 9. F

21. Find the indicated items on this map. In the space provided, write the letter that best identifies each point of interest. Note that not all sites on the map are used. (7 points)

1. G 2. O 3. E 4. U 5. B 6 T 7. Q

22. Read the following short paragraphs. Then complete the blank spaces logically with the appropriate form of the comparative or superlative to describe what you have just read. (5 points)

1. tan 2. más vieja/mayor 3. mejor 4. más joven/menor 5. tantas

23. Read this letter from students in a school here in the United States to students in a school in Santiago, Chile. Then answer the questions that follow in complete sentences in Spanish. (8 points)

Possible answers:
1. La profesora de los muchachos viajó a Chile el verano pasado. 2. Habló con la señora Triviño. 3. Quieren saber cuáles son las temperaturas mínimas y máximas de cada estación. 4. Las clases que todos tienen que estudiar son el inglés, las matemáticas y la historia.

24. In Spanish, write at least five complete sentences in which you tell about yourself and the past year. You may choose to tell what you will be doing during the coming summer, or any other information you would like. Include some of the following in your composition. (10 points)

Creative self-expression.